Nature Library

SEASHORE LIFE

Nature Library

SEASHORE LIFE

Andrew Campbell

Exeter Books

NEW YORK

Artists

Henry Barnet, John Beswick, Roger Gorringe, The Hayward Art Group,
Ken Lilly, Patricia Mynott, James Nicholls, Will Nickless,
George Thompson, The Tudor Art Agency Ltd.

Photographic acknowledgements

BIOFOTOS, FARNHAM 48, Heather Angel
12, 32, 35, 36, 38, 47, 59, 75, Ian Took 70;
BRUCE COLEMAN, UXBRIDGE: Adrian
Davies 74, Nicholas Devore 63, Giorgio Guako
73; CROSS SECTIONS: Bill Wood 68; HAM-
LYN GROUP PICTURE LIBRARY 6 – 7, 8, 11,
13 left, 13 right, 16, 22 top, 22 bottom, 23 top,
23 bottom, 24, 27, 33, 39, 44, 54, 55 top, 55
bottom, 56 top, 56 bottom, 57 top, 57 bottom,
60 bottom, 61; NATURAL HISTORY PHOTO-
GRAPHIC AGENCY, HYTHE: Anthony
Bannister 45, Brian Hawkes 10, 18, Peter
Johnson 76 – 77, Ivan Polunin 29 top, 29 bot-
tom, 30, 64, 65 top, 65 bottom, Bill Wood 62,
71 top, 71 centre, 71 bottom, 72; OXFORD
SCIENTIFIC FILMS 15, 49; SEAPHOT, BRIS-
TOL: Kim Westerskov 17, Walter Deas 69;
Z.E.F.A., LONDON: G. Marche 60 top.

Contents

Preface

The purpose of this book is to illustrate and describe the forms and habits of some of the world's seashore plants and animals, and to relate them to the conditions imposed by the environment.

Many animals living in the sea were first described by Aristotle. Centuries later, great expeditions were mounted by the expanding nations of Europe, such as that of James Cook to Australia and New Zealand in the eighteenth century. The results of investigations by naturalists in association with these voyages of discovery stimulated people like the Swede, Carl Linnaeus, to embark upon Systema Naturae, *a founding work of botany and zoology which attempts to classify all living things. By the middle of the nineteenth century many naturalists were describing and naming a flood of organisms new to science. These developments in biology inspired men such as Charles Darwin and Alfred Russell Wallace to develop the theory of evolution. Their pronouncements stimulated the need for experimental biology, and one area to benefit from this stimulus was marine biology.*

Laboratories and research vessels began to appear which were to transform man's understanding of the natural world in the sea. As the descriptions of species became more complete, so investigations into the habits of plants and animals and their mechanisms of dealing with environmental pressures were able to commence. Most of the discoveries made in the course of these investigations can be verified at first hand by anyone whose interest in the seashore goes beyond sunbathing on the beach.

Introduction

A mention of the seashore is sufficient to remind most people of happy holidays spent in fine summer weather amid great natural beauty. To such people the seashore would seem the ideal environment for an animal to live in. The reality is very different. Although a great variety of animals and plants inhabit the shore, they are able to do so only because they have adapted to withstand the extremely harsh conditions that prevail there.

The seashore is a boundary zone between the fully marine habitats of the open oceans or shallow seas and the terrestrial habitats of dry land. The sea itself provides an environment of great stability, where physical conditions such as temperature, salinity and availability of oxygen are all fairly constant. Marine organisms run no risk from desiccation. Land plants and animals are at risk from many dangers, having to endure wide temperature ranges, rainfall, flood, drought, winds and so on. The plants and animals which live on land have evolved to cope with such physical problems, but there are relatively few varieties which have done so. Of the twenty-five or so major groups or 'phyla' of animals recognized by scientists, only four, the chordates (amphibians, reptiles, birds and mammals), arthropods (insects, spiders, scorpions etc.), molluscs (snails and slugs) and annelids (earth-

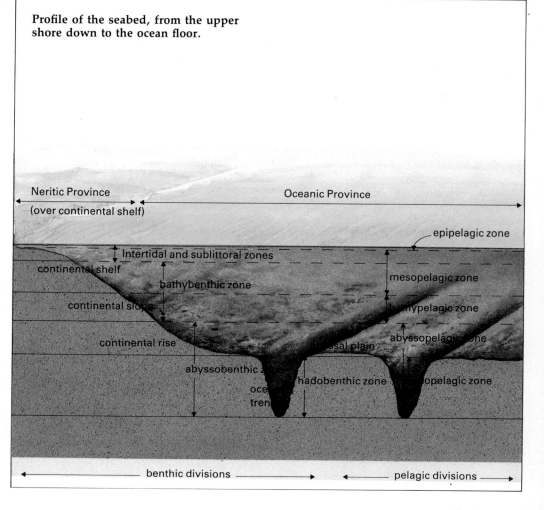

Profile of the seabed, from the upper shore down to the ocean floor.

Neritic Province
(over continental shelf)

Oceanic Province

epipelagic zone

Intertidal and sublittoral zones

continental shelf

bathybenthic zone

mesopelagic zone

continental slope

bathypelagic zone

continental rise

abyssal plain

abyssopelagic zone

abyssobenthic zone

hadobenthic zone

hadopelagic zone

oce
tren

benthic divisions

pelagic divisions

	Major Group of Organisms		Ocean/Sea	Shore	Dry Land
Plants	Bacteria				
	Fungi				
	Algae	Green			
		Brown			
		Red			
	Lichens				
	Mosses				
	Ferns				
	Higher Plants	Grasses			
		Herbs			
		Shrubs			
		Trees			
Animals	Sponges				
	Coelenterates				
	Sea Gooseberries				
	Flat worms				
	Ribbon worms				
	Round worms				
	Rotifers				
	Segmented worms	Rustle worms			
		Earth worms			
		Leeches			
	Moluscs	Minor types			
		Snails and slugs			
		Bivalves			
		Octopusses/Squid			
	Arthropods	Minor types			
		Crustaceans			
		Insects			
		Spiders etc			
	Bryozoans				
	Brachiopods				
	Arrow worms				
	Hemichordates				
	Chordates	Cartilaginous fishes			
		Bony fishes			
		Amphibia			
		Reptiles			
		Birds			
		Mammals			

The major groups of terrestrial and marine organisms; the chart shows to what extent they overlap on the shore.

worms) have developed to live successfully on land. We may, however, find representatives of all 25 of the groups in the sea, ranging from the minute single-celled protozoa through to the great whales.

The seashore is technically defined as that area lying between the highest point to which the tide flows and the lowest point to which it ebbs. Shore-dwelling organisms must be able to tolerate both terrestial and marine factors, since they are regularly covered and uncovered by the tidal movements. It has also been proposed, although now it is widely doubted, that the seashore provided a route for marine animals to colonize dry land. (It is more probable that the colonization of dry land was achieved via fresh water.)

Scientific interest in shores, then, is high. However, they are of great interest to non-specialists, too, for they provide an opportunity for the exploration and study of marine habitats and their inhabitants. Exploring a shore at low tide is the next best thing to diving in the sea itself.

The importance and interest of seashores is extended by the fact that they are an almost universal geographical feature. They occur in all continents, in all climates and in all oceans. They also occur as fossils, giving valuable evidence to geologists about the levels of the early seas of our planet. They are of economic importance in connection with fisheries, shipping and the exploitation of natural resources. They are also vulnerable to pollution and to contamination with man's waste.

Below: the sea is the origin of all forms of life. Around twenty-five major groups or 'phyla' of animals are recognized by biologists today, and every one of these is represented in the sea. Only four have succeeded in colonizing terrrestrial habitats. This diagram shows part of the complex process of evolution, covering the 30 million years from around 570 to 540 million years ago.

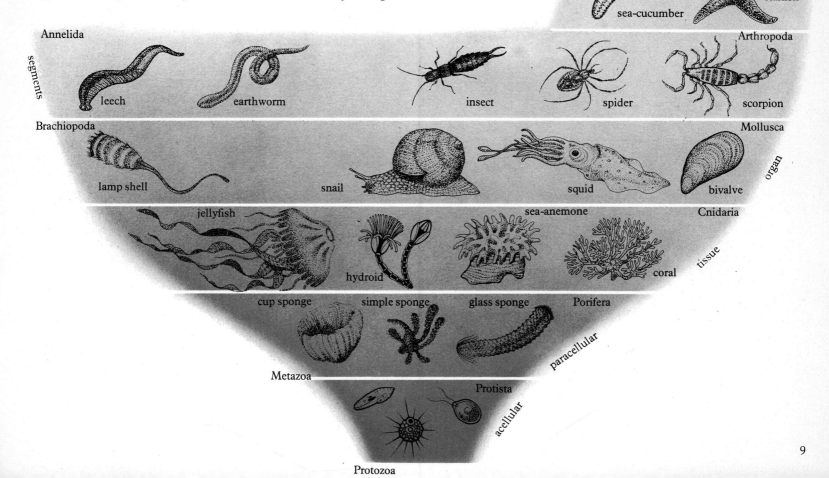

What is a Seashore?

We have already seen that the seashore is both the boundary of the land and the boundary of the sea. It is a narrow strip around our islands and continents, alternately dried by the sun and air, and wetted by the sea or the rain.

The form of any shore depends on its substrate and on the way it is affected by exposure to the seas. Of these, the nature of the substrate is the more important factor. It may be hard rock, soft rock, shingle, sand or mud, or combinations of two or more of these.

The substrate of the shore is moulded by the elements: wind, rain and sea are powerful natural agents that can wear a shore away; softer rocks in particular are vulnerable to this action. Equally the elements, particularly rain and sea, may deposit more substrate on a shore. This may be in the form of river-borne silt or particulate matter in the sea itself. Drifting currents along the coasts, together with wave action, can move particles from the finest silts to quite coarse shingle.

Left: **a shingle shore, showing the ridges left by the receding tides. Very few animals can tolerate the harsh conditions of shingle so there are no signs of zoned life.**

Arctic	Patagonian	West African	Caribbean
Californian	Panamic	Mediterranean	Magellanic

Above: **marine zoogeographical provinces of the world, as proposed by S. P. Woodward: at least 50% of the species in each of these provinces has to be peculiar to that province.**

Just as the nature of the substrate is of great importance in shaping a shore, so also are the characteristics of the seas which wash over it. The gravitational forces of the sun and moon pull on the water of the oceans in such a way that they produce tides. Tides are effectively movements of vast masses of water round the earth; they occur in such a way that at any given point on the globe there will be roughly two high tides separated by two low tides every twenty-four hours. The extent of tidal movement varies over a period of one lunar month (28 days) as well as in other cycles. Tides are not constant all over the world: they are influenced by a number of factors, in-

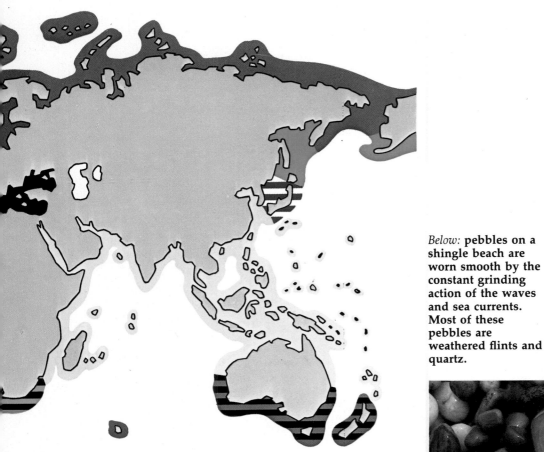

cluding variations in the depth of the seabed, submerged obstacles such as reefs, submarine ridges, and because interposing land masses can either amplify or compress the water movements.

Therefore, in some parts of the world we find very little tidal movement. The eastern Mediterranean and the central Red Sea have such restricted tides that the water level may appear to be constant, or to be affected more by other phenomena, such as changes in atmospheric pressure, than they are by tides proper. By contrast, there are places such as the Bristol Channel where the funnelling effect of the land masses of Wales and southwest England compress the tidal streams and amplify the tides, so that a tidal range of around 10 metres or more may be obtained.

Because of this there will be large shores in places with a great tidal range, and virtually no shore (in the strict sense of the word) in places where there is little or no tide. The top of the shore will obviously be exposed to the air for a much greater proportion of the 12-hour tidal cycle than the lower regions, so the conditions can vary greatly between top and bottom.

Below: **pebbles on a shingle beach are worn smooth by the constant grinding action of the waves and sea currents. Most of these pebbles are weathered flints and quartz.**

Marine zoogeographical provinces of the world

Australian	Peruvian
Indo-Pacific	Aleutian
Transatlantic	Boreal
South African	Japonic

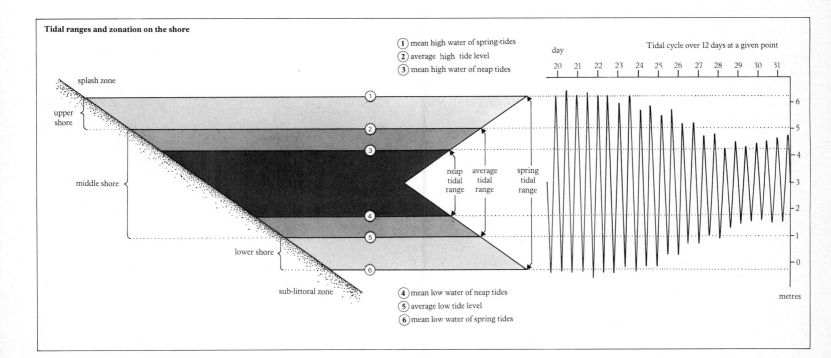

Tidal ranges and zonation on the shore

splash zone

upper shore

middle shore

lower shore

sub-littoral zone

(1) mean high water of spring-tides
(2) average high tide level
(3) mean high water of neap tides

neap tidal range — average tidal range — spring tidal range

(4) mean low water of neap tides
(5) average low tide level
(6) mean low water of spring tides

day

Tidal cycle over 12 days at a given point

20 21 22 23 24 25 26 27 28 29 30 31

6
5
4
3
2
1
0

metres

A harsh place to live

All forms of life are ultimately dependent on light, which provides energy for green plants to manufacture organic compounds such as sugars, and these in turn are utilized by animals. But there are other factors which are also crucially important, namely temperature, desiccation, water, salinity, substrate type and exposure.

The extent of the shore is governed by the height to which the tides rise and the depth to which they fall. If the shore is exposed to wind and wave action the water masses are driven further up and down the shore, and the influence of the sea on land is extended by the effects of spray. On a rocky shore the range of the tides will be clearly indicated by the plants and attached animals. A variety of lichens will exist at the top of the shore, and various algae will be found nearer to the extreme low tide mark. Not only will the extent of the shore be much greater in an exposed place, but the actual species of plants will differ between an exposed and a sheltered shore; some species are better adapted to withstand

Examples of how exposure can affect the life forms that predominate on zones of the shore within the same geographical area. *Left*: **zonation on an extremely exposed shore.** *Right*: **a very sheltered shore.** *Centre*: **a partly exposed shore.**

Below: **unlike shingle beaches, rocky shores immediately give an impression of flourishing life. Here zonation of yellow and black lichens, grey barnacles and brown seaweed can be clearly seen.**

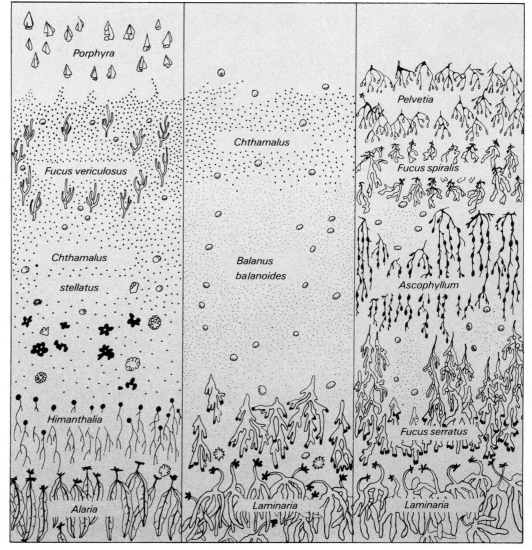

sun or the drying winds of the hot season. Some seaweeds have a layer of water-retaining tissue which protects the other tissues beneath from damage. In others a thick layer of slime reduces the effects of water loss. Thus the absence of delicate soft-bodied animals and of plants lacking water-retaining mechanisms denotes a position where desiccation seriously endangers live organisms.

Few shore-dwelling animals can regulate their body temperature. Most, particularly those which live attached to rocks and shells, are more or less obliged to accept the temperature of the surroundings, or they die. For some, however, there are other solutions. The barnacles, for example, can release a slow dribble of seawater from within their shell. As this evaporates on their outer surface it cools the shells, in the same way as sweat cools the human body. Periods of unusually hot or unusually cold weather nearly always kill the animal. When covered by the sea, shore animals are protected by the relatively constant temperature of seawater; when exposed to air they are at the mercy of numerous factors.

The aspect of a shore, i.e. the direction it faces, and the topography of the land behind it – cliffs, flat plains or whatever – all regulate the amount of light it receives, and this governs the health of growing plants.

Left: **layers of algae showing the shore zonation on an exposed section of sea wall: green seaweeds at the top are followed by brown seaweeds, with the red kinds becoming increasingly prominent towards the base.**

Below: **Dog Whelk *(Nucella lapillus)* feeding on Acorn Barnacles.**

the severe mechanical action and turbulence of exposed habitats, whilst others require a tranquil habitat in which to live out their lives. Because of the difficulties of measuring exposure by purely physical means, bearing in mind that weather patterns tend to be very variable, scientists have adopted a principle of using the organisms of shores to indicate reliably the degree of exposure.

The effects of heat, wind and desiccation are all interrelated. Drying out is a great risk for all shore-dwellers, and those animals that have colonized the highest positions on the shore have water-retaining mechanisms such as shells or other impermeable outer coverings. Alternatively, behaviour patterns such as shade-seeking may help animals to escape the worst effects of the midday

The food chain

Conditions on seashores are more extreme than in almost all other environments. These physical conditions are, however, not the only factors that control the ultimate development of shore life; just as important are the interrelationships of the organisms that dwell there. Living organisms occupy space and need food. They produce waste materials; they respire and reproduce. All these activities, known as biotic factors, have effects upon their neighbours.

The first and perhaps greatest factor is food. All animals need food, and this comes either directly or indirectly from plants. Sunlight provides the energy needed for all forms of life. Green plants harness this energy and convert it to organic materials such as sugars, using mineral salts and water in the presence of chlorophyll. The most productive of all green plants in the sea are to be found drifting by the million in the surface waters of the oceans and shallow seas: there they are bathed in sunlight and supplied with nutrient mineral salts from the vast reserves of the oceans. These drifting plants form a vital community in the sea: that of the **phytoplankton**. There are many members of the phytoplankton, but the most important ones are two groups of microscopic plants – diatoms and dinoflagellates. Every drop of surface seawater is likely to contain a few,

Right: **some examples of inshore phytoplankton.** *Top:* **Chaetoceros decipiens,** **a diatom.** *Lower left:* **Peridinium depressum, a dinoflagellate.** *Lower right:* **another dinoflagellate, Noctiluca scintillans, a phosphorescent species that can turn the sea red, and may be left behind as a red scum on rocks. All magnified approximately 375 times.**

Below: **some of the small organisms predominant in shore plankton.**

although their abundance varies according to the time of year and to other circumstances. When these plants are completely absent the seawater is unproductive.

The tides that wash up and down the shores bring the phytoplankton directly to the shore-dwelling organisms. Some of these have efficient filters and can exploit it directly, but diatoms and dinoflagellates are too small for many to deal with. There is a further community of drifting animals the **zooplankton**, consisting both of adults drifting in their own right as members of the plankton (e.g. the copepods and the krill) and of

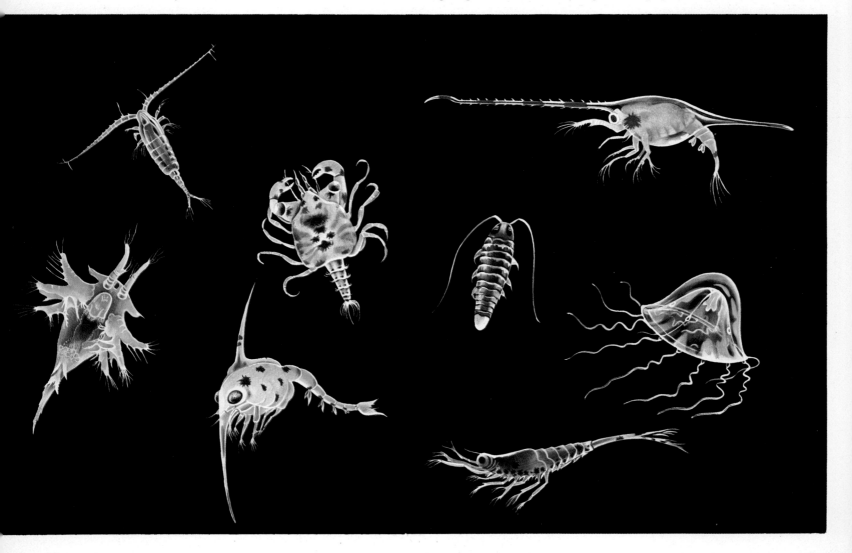

the larvae of bottom-dwelling and shore-dwelling animals. Many of these zooplankton are able to filter off the phytoplankton; it is often these first grazers that subsequently form a food supply for the filter-feeding shore-dwellers.

So it is that members of almost all groups of animals have shore-dwelling representatives which strain the waters of the tides in search of food. Many of these animals are unable to move about at all as adults, or only to a very limited extent: feeding on suspended material in this way is their only method.

The more mobile invertebrates and the fishes are able to prey upon a variety of animals, both smaller and larger. This they may do by more conventional means, using an assortment of trapping tentacles, teeth and jaws.

A summary diagram called a food web can be constructed to show the complex interrelationship of the shore-dwelling organisms, and it will be seen from this that the life in the seas beyond the shore is involved as well, so that a seashore may not be the self-contained biological system that it at first appears to be. Obviously if there is competition to gain food, then those best able to exploit the source will survive, whilst those less able may not do so.

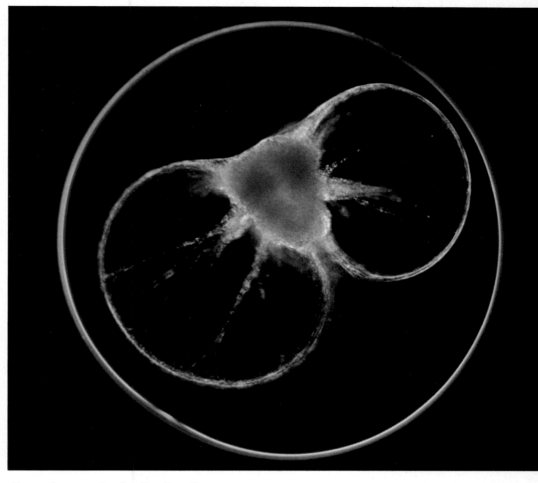

Above: **photograph of a dinoflagellate.**

Below: **food web in a marine community. The many members of the phytoplankton represent an extremely valuable food resource, but the larger animals cannot** feed directly on microscopic organisms. There is another community, the zooplankton, which consists of filter-feeding animals, and these are the prey of many shore-dwelling species. All marine animals depend on phytoplankton either directly or indirectly for their food source at some time in their life-cycles.

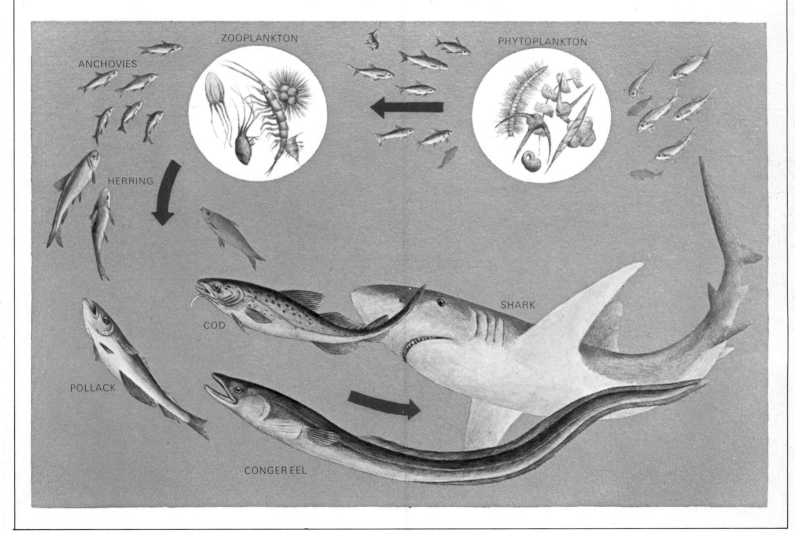

The never-ending fight for life

Competition for food within a community of organisms may seem the most obvious form of biological competition, but it is not the only one.

Competition for space is great, especially in a community where so many organisms need attachment or ground space. Quite apart from the algae, many animals are physically attached to the hard shore. These include those forms such as sponges, hydroids, corals, some tube-worms, barnacles, oysters, sea-mats (bryozoans) and sea-squirts which could not move about even if they wanted to. Then there are the sedentary slow-moving invertebrates which live attached to rocks by a sucker-disc or sucker-foot: examples are the sea-anemones, many sea-snails, especially the limpets and ormers (abalones), starfish and sea-urchins. All of these animals, along with the plants, must hold on to the rocks to prevent being washed away into unsuitable situations, and in many cases the adaptation they have made to compensate for the difficult physical conditions has forced them to colonize a particular level on the shore. Species which successfully colonize low levels of the shore, but which cannot withstand the conditions further up, force those which can do so to take up a higher position, or die through lack of any other alternative.

Plants compete for light not only amongst themselves, but with animals such as sponges and sea-squirts. Often the animals are poor competitors, hence sponges may be rare on the lower shore in open illuminated places, but abundant in caves, where plants cannot survive.

Mobile animals are not restricted to one place, but can move about to find optimum conditions. Thus at some times particular species may appear scarce in a given place, whilst at others they may appear plentiful. However, the relative abundance of organisms on a shore is more usually the result of the recruitment of new individuals to the population and

Amphianthus dohrni on *Eunicella verrucosa*

Metridium senile

pink form

white form

Calliactis parasitica on shell occupied by *Eupagurus bernhardus*

Adamsia palliata on shell occupied by *Eupagurus prideauxi*

Above: **the struggle for survival in coastal waters is intense, and this has led to the evolution of strange relationships between very different animals. For example, certain sea-anemones may take up residence on old mollusc shells occupied by hermit crabs: the anemone protects the crab from predators such as *Octopus* and also obtains scraps of food made available by the crab. *Amphianthus* enters into a relationship with the sea-fan *Eunicella*. *Metridium* has many fine tentacles with which it strains suspended food matter from the water.**

Left: **limpets. The one on its back is showing its powerful sucker-foot ringed by its gills, with its head and tentacles protruding to the left.**

the mortality of older ones. Mortality can be due to a number of factors – predation, death from food shortages, severe physical conditions, and so on.

For attached organisms that are unable to move in any direction, the choice of a site in which to live will clearly be of the utmost importance. Many attached marine animals have a complex life cycle with a free-swimming larval phase which feeds in the plankton in a way different from the adult form, thus avoiding competition with its parents for living space and for food. It is also able to effect dispersal because it is mobile. At the end of this larval planktonic life, some important choices have to be made. The terminal larval stages of animals such as barnacles, sea-mats and oysters, all of which live physically attached as adults, have the necessary sense organs to identify a suitable spot. Factors such as the texture of the substratum and the presence or absence of adults are all taken into account.

Below: crayfish often form social groups. **Here a number are sheltering in a small cave in New Zealand waters. Notice also the encrusting sponges and other organisms hanging from the rocks.**

Below: **adult barnacles among juveniles. The Acorn Barnacle *(Balanus balanoides)* can tolerate colder water than the Star Barnacle *(Chthamalus montagui),* and can thus be found in profusion in cooler** northern waters where the latter is absent. **Where conditions exist in which both species can flourish, the Star Barnacle usually occupies the site at the expense of its relative.**

Chthamalus montagui

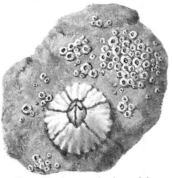

Semibalanus balanoides

Living space can be a problem for highly mobile animals too. Recent research on coral reefs has shown that there are only a limited number of hiding places suitable for fishes sheltering from predators. A swim around a reef, at any time of the day or night, shows these places to be occupied, but not always by the same individuals or species of fish. Scientists have coined the term 'resource sharing' for this phenomenon. By day, nocturnal fishes shelter in the crevices and caverns of the reef; at dusk they venture forth to feed and their places are taken by the diurnal fish. At dawn the process is reversed.

The world's shores – how they differ

Because of the vast total length of the world's coastlines, and the fact that land masses occur in every latitude and in a variety of rock forms, there is an almost endless variety of shores in the world. Climate and geology are two important factors in determining shore type; so are tidal range and, in the case of reefs, the coral animals. The commonest substrates are rocks, sand, mud, shingle and coral reef. Other seashore habitats are provided by mangrove swamps, artificial shores such as piers, pilings and breakwaters, and reefs formed by organisms other than coral, e.g. by polchaete worms such as *Sabellaria alveolata* and *Mercierella enigmatica*.

Substrate type is probably the principal determining factor. Hard rocks such as granite will endure for a very long time, withstanding the erosion of wind, rain and seawater. They will permit attached animals to become well established, and such shores will often carry a thick flora and fauna, as long as other conditions permit. Soft rocks such as chalk and shale are easily eroded; shores made from these materials may support only a light flora and fauna, because no organism is likely to find purchase there for a long period. These softer rocks are favourable

Above: **when viewed from a distance, sandy and muddy shores may appear to be devoid of life. However, solid objects such as piles provide a substratum for barnacles which would otherwise be unable to colonize the area.**

Right: **the ocean currents of the world. The temperature of the waters that wash any seashore exerts a profound influence on the nature of the plants and animals that may live there. Corals inhabit the eastern seaboards of the continents where these are washed with warm water from the tropics.**

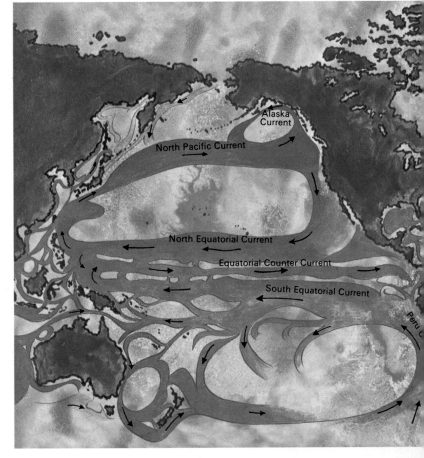

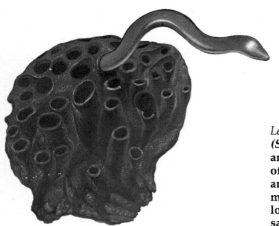

Left: **Mason Worm (Sabellaria).** This animal builds a tube of sand and shell around its body; it may be found on the lower sections of sandy and muddy shores, near the low water mark.

for burrowing and drilling animals, as they are easier to attack. Shingle beaches support virtually no life, partly because they are nearly always on the move due to the action of waves and current; they are therefore unstable and difficult to colonize. Further, the action of pebbles being washed around by heavy waves is fatal to soft-bodied organisms, which become pulped.

Sandy and muddy shores can support large numbers of organisms if conditions are favourable, but compared with rocky shores they do not support such a varied fauna. This is because there is no firm point of attachment for animals that need it: consequently the organisms colonizing these shores are restricted to those which can nestle between the grains of the substrate or burrow into it. Burrowing worms and bivalves and some crusta-

Right and above right: **two of the world's more exotic types of shore. Coral reefs like that shown above right grow very slowly but are easily destroyed by thoughtless exploitation such as mineral extraction. Mangrove swamps such as that shown right are now attracting more scientific interest than formerly.**

ceans (e.g. shrimps) flourish here, but forms like the large algae, sponges, limpets, barnacles and sea-mats and sea-squirts are excluded unless they can obtain a foothold on some other organism, such as a sea-grass or mangrove tree, which is able to colonize the area by virtue of its root system.

Coral reefs can be regarded as seashores in which the substrate is provided by the dominant animals. Coral polyps secrete a hard limestone skeleton round the outside of their bodies, and it is the accumulation of these skeletons over vast periods of time, along with the hard parts of various associated organisms, that leads to the aggregation of coral limestone to form a reef. Only the coral polyps on the outside of the reef are alive: in fact the reef is a massive calcareous deposit, with a thin veneer of living tissue on the outside, continuing the process of limestone secretion.

Piers, pilings and other man-made structures such as wrecked ships may provide artificial shores. These have been used by scientists for research into the processes of colonization by shore-dwelling animals. Research into coral reefs has been greatly aided by studies of such structures.

East Greenland Current

Labrador Current

North Atlantic Current

Gulf Stream

Canary Current

North Equatorial Current

South Equatorial Current

North Equatorial Current

Equatorial Counter Current

South Equatorial Current

Brazil Current

Falkland Current

West Wind Drift

Seaweeds and their colours

From a distance, many rocky shores appear discoloured by the organisms which grow on them. The large algae of the shore, technically known as macro-algae to distinguish them from their smaller, frequently microscopic, relatives in the plankton, are one of the main sources of seashore colour. Temperate shores are generally tinged with brown at low tide because of the preponderance of large brown algae. The rocky floor of very shallow seas is predominantly pinkish-red, due to the red algae which flourish in this habitat. The green algae occur on many temperate shores, but they are most conspicuous on tropical rocky shores, such as those of east Africa, where strong illumination and warm seawater favour their development.

There are a number of types of algae, but the greens, browns and reds are the most conspicuous. The difference between them lies in the fact that in the green variety there is no accessory pigment masking the green chlorophyll. Macroscopic green algae occur in a number of forms. The larger ones appear either as floating or attached fronds or filaments, e.g. the sea lettuce *Ulva* or the tubular *Enteromorpha*. These have a relatively simple structure of thin tissue making up the frond, with a rudimentary holdfast. Similar weeds occur on shores throughout the world. Others, such as *Codium*, *Valonia* and *Dasycladus* may comprise quite robust branching, club-like or tubular growths. One type of *Codium* is particularly common on Mediterranean shores. Then there are types such as *Cladophora* and *Bryopsis* which have delicate branching fronds. Some varieties like *Acetabularia* and *Halimeda* have strangely formed bodies stiffened by deposits of chalky material.

The reason for the different colours of the algae basically relates to the manner in which sunlight is affected on passing through seawater. When light is split into its component colours we see it as the familiar spectrum of rainbow colours – red, orange, yellow, green, blue, indigo and violet. The light at the red end of the spectrum does not penetrate seawater as well as the light at the blue end, so that to a diver at 10 meters everything seems tinged with blue. Algae need a good source of light for photosynthesis, but when they are covered by seawater it is interrupted by the filtering off of the red end of the spectrum. Thus the brown algae have evolved an accessory pigment, fucoxanthin, which hides the green of the chlorophyll; similarly the red algae have evolved a red pigment, rhodophycin, which again has masked the green. These brown and red pigments improve the efficiency of photosynthesis of the algae in deep water. In the strong light of the tropics, many green algae flourish because they get enough light without accessory pigments.

Seawater acts as a filter which screens off the light, starting at the red end of the spectrum. Blue light penetrates deepest, but below about 1000 metres no light at all can penetrate even the purest seawater. This means that organisms that dwell below the surface waters have developed accessory pigments in order to be able to make efficient use of the limited available light.

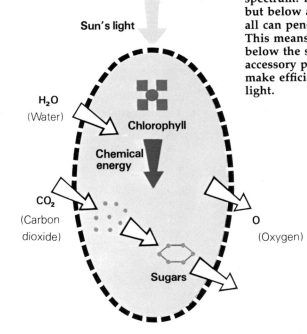

The process of photosynthesis shown in diagrammatic form: water and carbon dioxide are combined in the presence of chlorophyll (which gives plants their green coloration) to produce the sugars that sustain the plant. Oxygen is a by-product.

Sun's light

H_2O
(Water)

Chlorophyll

Chemical energy

CO_2
(Carbon dioxide)

O
(Oxygen)

Sugars

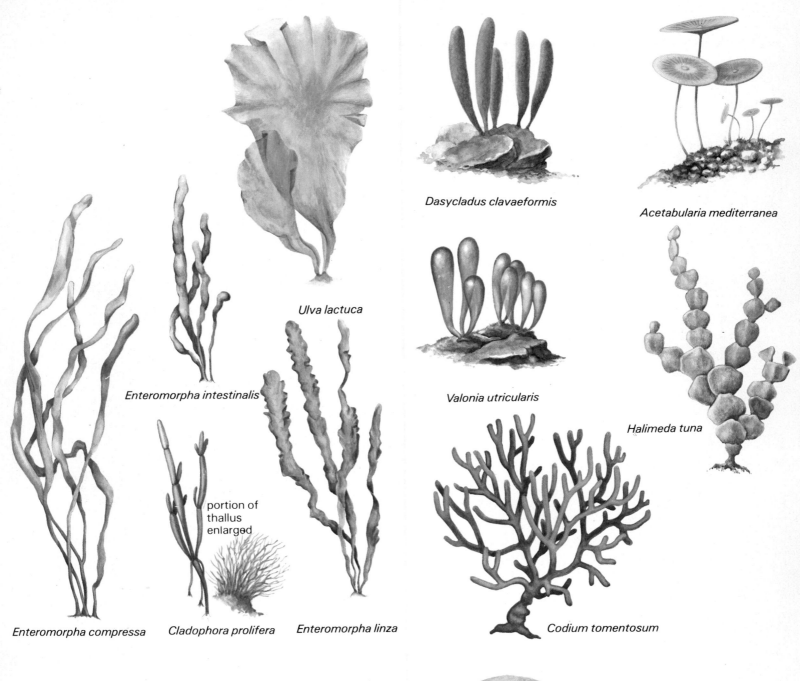

Ulva lactuca

Enteromorpha intestinalis

Dasycladus clavaeformis

Acetabularia mediterranea

Valonia utricularis

Halimeda tuna

portion of thallus enlarged

Enteromorpha compressa

Cladophora prolifera

Enteromorpha linza

Codium tomentosum

Codium bursa

Below: one of the green algae, **Enteromorpha intestinalis**, growing in profusion on a cliff face on the upper shore. The plant has succeeded in establishing itself in every crevice reached by the seawater.

Above: a selection of green algae, showing some of the widely differing growth forms which enable them to occupy different habitats on the shore and in shallow water.

The brown seaweeds

Laminaria digitata

Sargassum vulgare

Laminaria saccharina

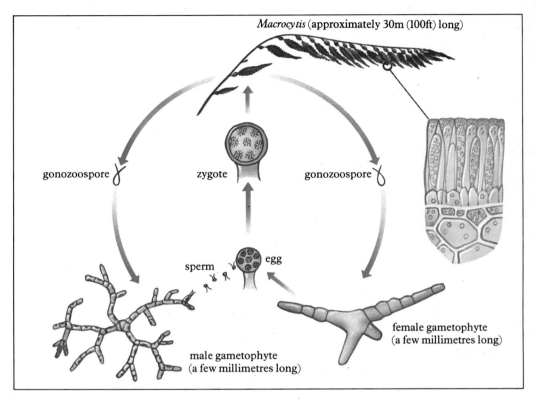

Macrocytis (approximately 30m (100ft) long)

gonozoospore

zygote

gonozoospore

sperm

egg

male gametophyte
(a few millimetres long)

female gametophyte
(a few millimetres long)

like, but they play no part in supplying the plant with food, as do the roots of land plants. The holdfast has to be strong in order to anchor the plant in position. Many small animals take up residence in the holdfasts and find a secure home there.

Other brown algae have delicate feathery fronds, e.g. *Desmarestia* and *Arthrocladia*. In *Sargassum* and *Cystoseira*, which are common on many tropical shores, the

Life-cycle of one of the brown algae. At high tide reproductive spores (gonozoospores) are washed from the fronds of the sporophyte to settle on the seabed, where they give rise to male or female gametophytes. Male gametophytes produce sperms which swim to the females, and these produce oogonia, each with one egg; after fertilization the embryo divides and grows into a new sporophyte.

These are the algae that are most familiar to visitors at temperate seasides, but they also occur in great quantities in the cooler seas of the world where the water is shallow enough, and where there is a suitable hard substrate for them to gain attachment. The brown macro-algae grow in many shapes and sizes from the small growths encrusting rocks, like *Ralfsia*, through to the enormous kelps like *Macrocytis* of the Pacific, which may reach a length of up to 30 meters. The body of an alga is known as the *thallus*. Each thallus is composed of a frond and a holdfast. In the brown algae the frond is often straplike or flat and branching. Straplike growths are characteristic of types such as the kelps (e.g. *Laminaria*), while in the wracks (e.g. *Fucus*) the flattened frond is regularly branched. The holdfasts of algae such as these are superficially root-

frond is branched many times and there may be leaflike structures on the ends. The whole frond, however, participates in the process of photosynthesis, not just the leaflike growths. A few types of brown algae have peculiarly shaped bodies. Examples are the fanlike *Padina* and the rounded *Colpomenia*; *Himanthalia* has rounded button-like growths from which arise long thin straplike fronds in the summer. Some of the wracks, e.g. *Fucus vesiculosus* and species of *Sargassum* have gas-filled bladders which cause the weeds to float. The generally slimy feeling of these algae is due to the secretion of mucus by the frond. This mucus lubricates the fronds as they wash back and forth over themselves and the rocks, and it also plays a vital role in reducing water loss and hence desiccation when the algae are exposed to air by the falling tide. Some species like *Pelvetia canaliculata* can withstand the loss of a considerable quantity of water from their bodies before they die, but others like *Laminaria saccharina* cannot. This is why *Pelvetia* tends to be found near the top of a rocky shore and *Laminaria* near the bottom.

Many brown algae have swollen bodies on their fronds at certain times of the year. These are the reproductive bodies, and they are not the same as the flotation structures which occur on some species. The reproductive bodies are called conceptacles and contain male or female structures. Sperm are liberated from the male bodies and swim through the seawater attracted by the female bodies, which they eventually fertilize. A drifting embryo may then be produced which passes through the sea until it encounters a suitable hard substrate to which it can attach itself and grow into a new adult.

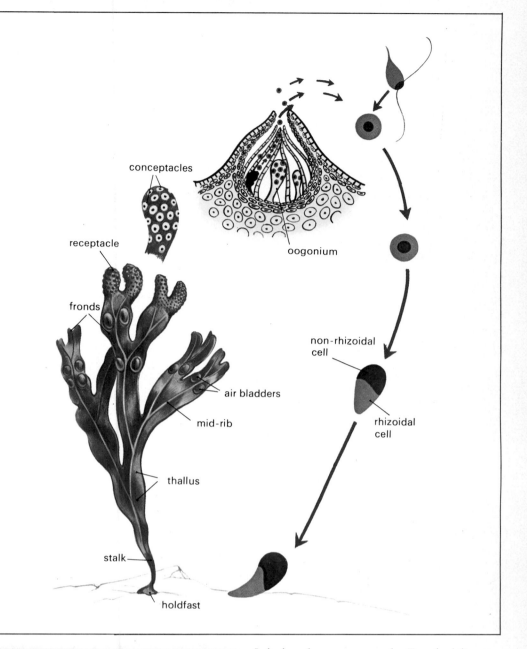

Left: **four brown seaweeds.** *Top, far left –* **Channelled Wrack (Pelvetia canaliculata),** which can be found on the upper shore. *Bottom, far left –* **Spiral Wrack (Fucus spiralis);** the tips are swollen conceptacles and the spotted parts are reproductive organs containing either sperm or eggs. *Left –* **Bladder Wrack (Fucus vesiculosus),** a typical plant of the middle shore; the air-filled bladders are for buoyancy. The life-cycle of this seaweed is illustrated above. *Below left –* **Serrated Wrack (Fucus serratus),** a seaweed of the lower middle shore.

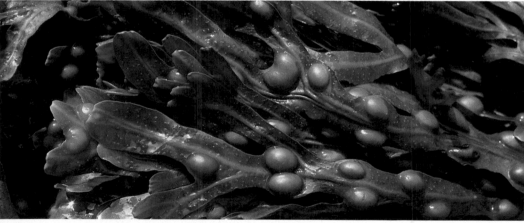

Cystoseira baccata

The red seaweeds

The red algae include some of the most beautiful marine plants. Generally they do not reach a great size, and despite their name 'red' they cover a wide range of colours from very pale greyish-pink through shocking pink to red and very dark, almost brown red.

These algae are represented on the shore by a range of species that grow attached to rocks, shells and even other algae. They are quite well represented in almost all latitudes and show an extensive range of form and growth habits. To appreciate fully the red algae it is necessary to go snorkelling or diving in shallow offshore water. These plants flourish down to about 10 meters and may be found at greater depths.

On many temperate rocky shores, the encrusting chalky red forms such as *Lithothamnion* and *Phymatolithon* smother the rocks with their flat growths. Other

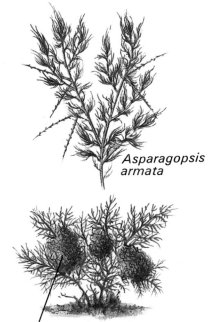

Asparagopsis armata

Falkenbergia rufolanosa growing on another alga

forms of *Lithothamnion* are found on the shallow seabed and are even dredged as marl, which is used in the construction industry as ballast.

On coral reefs, where the reef mass is formed from the accumulated skeletons of generations of coral polyps, calcareous red algae thrive. This is particularly so in the most exposed zone, the surf-washed algal ridge. Here, only those plants with massive skeletons can survive the crashing breakers, their photosynthetic tissue reinforced by calcareous skeletal elements which themselves make no mean contribution to the development of the reef, adding to the accreted limestone and knitting together the coral skeletons. *Lithothamnion* and *Porolithon* are important examples.

Not all calcareous algae are flat or encrusting; many, like *Corallina*, are filamentous, delicate and dividing into

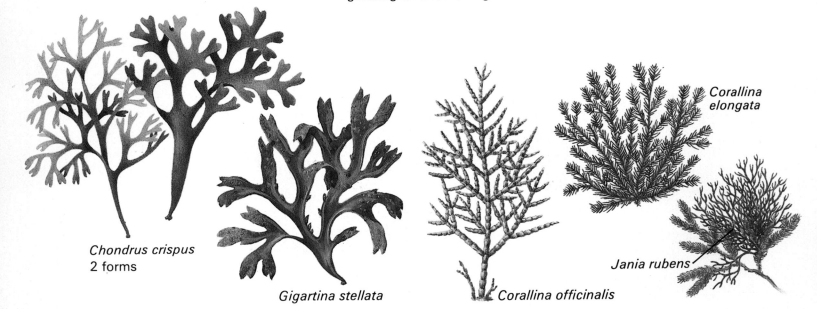

Chondrus crispus 2 forms

Gigartina stellata

Corallina officinalis

Corallina elongata

Jania rubens

branches and branchlets, each of which is supported by a number of minute skeletal segments. The majority of red algal species are, however, not calcareous and have relatively soft fronds, often delicately divided. Examples of these are *Heterosiphonia* and *Polysiphonia*. Other types are more leaf-like, e.g. *Apoglossum*, *Hypoglossum*, *Delesseria* and *Phycodrys*. The flat slimy purplish-red growths of *Porphyra* are simple in outline and very different in appearance from some of the other species; in some places *Porphyra* is cooked and eaten as laver bread. It is not the only alga to be eaten: in Eire *Chondrus crispus* and *Gigartina stellata* are harvested and prepared together as Irish Moss or Carragheen. Algae are regarded by many people as an important source of minerals, and brown algae such as *Laminaria* are processed into kelp tablets for ready consumption.

Opposite page, bottom: **A Rough-stalked Kelp with epiphytic red seaweeds growing along its stipe. Red seaweeds can be difficult to identify, but these are mostly *Rhodymenia palmata*.**

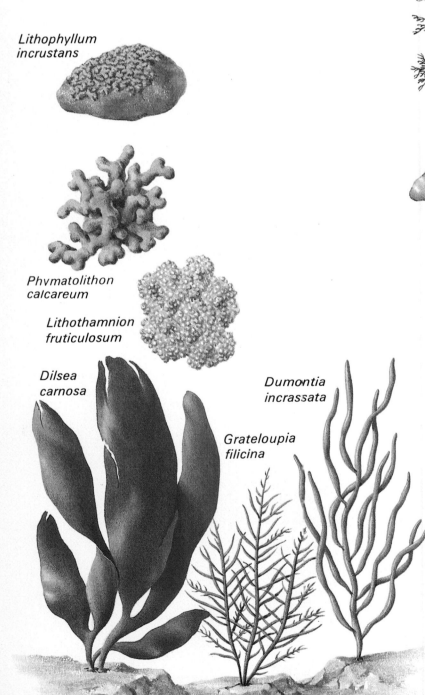

Lithophyllum incrustans

Phymatolithon calcareum

Lithothamnion fruticulosum

Dilsea carnosa

Dumontia incrassata

Grateloupia filicina

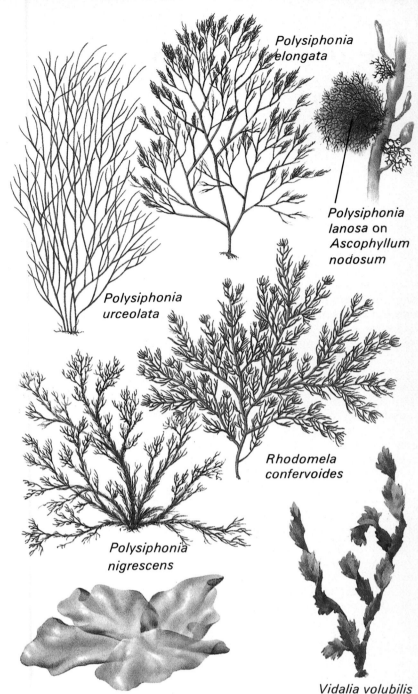

Polysiphonia elongata

Polysiphonia lanosa on *Ascophyllum nodosum*

Polysiphonia urceolata

Rhodomela confervoides

Polysiphonia nigrescens

Vidalia volubilis

Porphyra umbilicalis

The colour of red seaweeds varies from pale pink to deep brownish-red; some examples are shown on this and the opposite page.

A number of red algae live on the outside of other species of seaweed. Some species of *Polysiphonia*, e.g. *P. lanosa*, grow in tufts on the outsides of larger algae, such as the brown *Ascophyllum*. Like most algae, *Asparagopsis armata* exists as two alternating generations – a spore-producing, asexually reproducing generation and a gamete-forming, sexually reproducing generation. The two generations are physically different from each other, and before it was realized that they were different forms of the same species they were given different names, *Asparagopsis* for the gamete-producing phase and *Falkenbergia* for the spore-producing phase. The former is independent, while the latter is to be found growing on the outside of other algal species.

Sea-grasses

Apart from the mangroves, the sea-grasses are the only higher plants which have developed to live in the sea. They are relatives of the familiar land grasses, and this relationship is reflected in the form of the flowers and the flattened, veined, lance-shaped leaves. Unlike the algae the sea-grasses have been very successful in colonizing the sandy bottoms of lagoons and shallow seas. They do occur on the shore, but usually towards the low-tide mark. Sea-grasses are a relatively small group of plants, but a number of species are recognized from around the world.

In temperate waters they sometimes form large sea-grass beds, but they are more conspicuous in the warmer seas. In the Mediterranean there are extensive beds of *Posidonia oceanica* which form the basis for quite complex communities of organisms. Another species of *Posidonia* occurs in Australia. Extensive beds of *Cymodocea* and *Thallassia* occur along the sandy shores of the Indian Ocean, e.g. in East Africa, as well as in the Red Sea. Sea-grasses are common in the Caribbean.

Once the sea-grasses have colonized the sand, their roots stabilize it and allow other organisms such as burrowing invertebrates to move in. Algae, which are excluded from such habitats because of the lack of a hard substrate, may actually develop on the sea-grass leaves themselves. One such alga is *Fosliella farinosa*, a flat calcareous red form. Hydroids, sea-anemones and bryozoan colonies may also develop on the sea-grass leaves. The sea-grasses themselves form a food source for certain specialized herbivores: the dugong or sea-cow of the Indian and Pacific Oceans grazes on the sea-grass beds there.

A visitor to a sea-grass bed will probably be impressed with the wealth of rotting vegetation that lies on the sea-floor. This provides a source of food for invertebrate detrital feeders, but because of the fibrous nature of the leaves the decaying vegetation may take some time to disappear. It may get washed up in vast quantities in stormy weather, and on islands where litter for animals is short it has been used as bedding by farmers. The species of *Posidonia* produce such strong fibres that these lie on the seabed for a long time and in many cases the repeated action of the waves washing back and forth rolls these fibres up into round balls, up to the size of a tennis ball. Such sea-grass balls are a familiar sight in the Mediterranean and on the southern coasts of Australia.

The sea-grasses are anchored in the sand by true roots. Their flowers, like those of the land grasses, are not conspicuous, and they are fertilized by water-borne pollen.

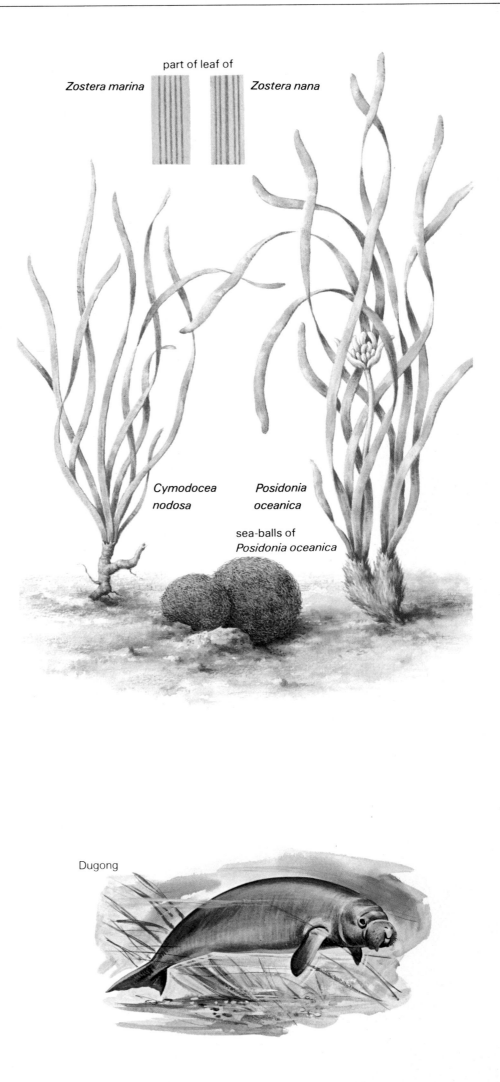

part of leaf of

Zostera marina   Zostera nana

Cymodocea
nodosa

Posidonia
oceanica

sea-balls of
Posidonia oceanica

Dugong

Mangroves

The word mangrove denotes a tree belonging to either of two genera, *Rhizophora* or *Bruguiera*; but it is also used in a looser sense to refer to other types of trees growing in seawater, as well as to the specialized 'woodland' community which the mangrove trees form. Apart from the sea-grasses, the mangroves are the only higher plants which can tolerate salt water. They are restricted in their distribution to warm tropical regions (see map) and they may grow on the coast or line the estuaries of rivers in the tropics. Trees such as this play an important role in stabilizing the land and reducing coastal erosion. Further, in some countries they are an important source of timber.

In order to live on the shore and in shallow water mangroves have adapted in various ways. These include the development of prop roots in the genus *Rhizophora* which help to stabilize the trees in the soft substrates which they characteristically inhabit. Mangroves flourish in coastal silts, clays and sands, although pure sand is rarely colonized. Seed distribution is by water, and again in *Rhizophora* we see specializations: here the seeds begin to germinate and develop whilst the fruit is still attached to the parent tree. The rootlet becomes long and pendant and when the embryonic plant drops off, it plunges into the substrate like a spear, to establish itself near the parent. Alternatively, being resistant to salt water, they may float in the sea for some time before being deposited somewhere, often far away, where they can continue development.

In many parts of the world mangroves form a narrow fringe of vegetation fronting the sea and joining with more typical terrestrial communities behind. In some cases, however, a zonation of mangrove trees running from just below the low water mark up to the top of the shore may be encountered, according to the ability of the plants in question to tolerate immersion in salt water. The succession obtained can be quite complex.

Some of the animals that inhabit mangrove communities are described on page 64.

Above right: **The pendulous seeds of *Rhizophora* begin development whilst still attached to the parent. When they fall off they frequently embed themselves in the mud ready for growth.**

Right: **Here the aerial roots, or 'pneumatophores', rise above the mud of the swamp. They assist in respiration and provide a subtrate for the attachment of other organisms.**

Sponges

The animal kingdom comprises a vast array of life-forms, from the lowly single-celled protozoa like *Amoeba* to the most complex animal of all – Man himself. Zoologists have grouped the animals into categories called 'phyla' (singular 'phylum'), and animals are placed together in a phylum if they are considered to have had a common evolutionary origin. The various phyla display different levels of organization: single-celled, many-celled, cells grouped into two layers, or three, lacking or possessing a cavity within the body, and so on. Apart from the protozoa, which are beyond the scope of this book, the

Spongia officinalis

Verongia aerophoba

Ircinia fasciculata

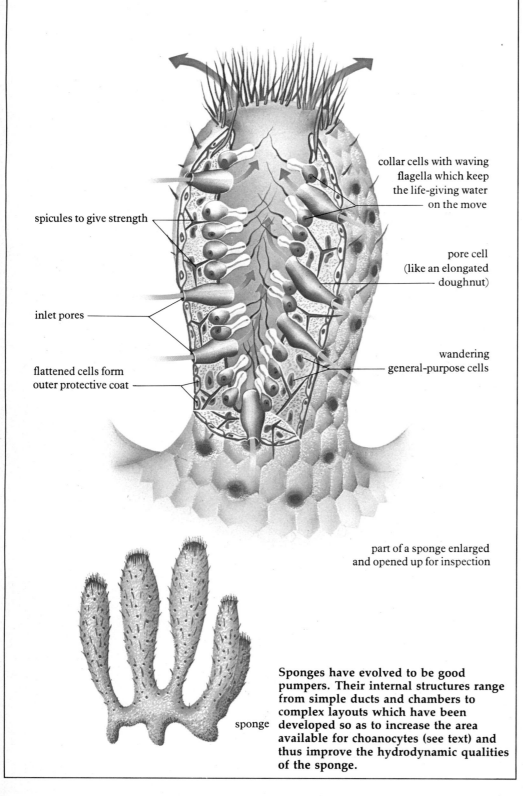

spicules to give strength

inlet pores

flattened cells form
outer protective coat

collar cells with waving
flagella which keep
the life-giving water
on the move

pore cell
(like an elongated
doughnut)

wandering
general-purpose cells

part of a sponge enlarged
and opened up for inspection

sponge

Sponges have evolved to be good pumpers. Their internal structures range from simple ducts and chambers to complex layouts which have been developed so as to increase the area available for choanocytes (see text) and thus improve the hydrodynamic qualities of the sponge.

sponges are considered to be amongst the most simple animals.

Sponges have bodies made up of many cells, but although they are numerous these cells occur in only a few types. The bodies are generally encrusting, growing over rocks and other organisms, or erect and flask-shaped or goblet-shaped. Many sponges are relatively soft and pliable, but some are hard and stiff, and their surfaces may be abrasive or sharp with minute or larger thorny projections.

These animals are classified by zoologists according to the type of skeleton that they possess. Members of the class Calcarea contain chalky spicules only. Generally these types are small and pale in colour, preferring shady places away from strong illumination. *Sycon* is an example, with a characteristic crown of spicules surrounding the exhalent opening at one end of the body. Another class, the Demospongiae, have a skeleton which may include spicules of silica, or may consist entirely of horny filaments of a special substance called spongin, or be a mixture of spongin and spicules. An example of the second type is *Spongia*, the bath sponge; the object that is used in the bathroom is the horny skeleton after it has been cleaned of all living tissue, and then dried. In various parts of the Mediterranean, and in other regions of the world, the preparation of this type of sponge is an important industry. *Verongia* also has a skeleton of horny filaments only, but its growth form is pillar-like. The encrusting *Halichondria*, familiar on the lower shores of many rocky temperate beaches, and *Hymeniacidon* have a skeleton which is a mixture of spicules and fibres.

Sponges are suspension feeders – they draw quantities of seawater into their bodies via minute pores called ostia. These are their inhalent openings. Food particles and oxygen in solution are extracted from the water as it passes through the sponge body. The water then flows into the main inner cavity, the paragaster, and then leaves via the osculum or exhalent pore. All sponges have many ostia; some species have a single osculum, others have many. The seawater is pumped through the body by special cells which line its inner walls. These cells, known as choanocytes, are equipped with cilia which beat back and forth to drive water currents, and with special collars which are thought to be important in the absorption of food.

Reproduction is by both asexual and sexual means. In many cases asexual overwintering bodies called gemmules are formed within the tissue of the sponge. These survive autumnal decline and start new growth the following spring. In other cases simple male and female organs develop and cross-fertilization leads to a simple free-swimming larva, which after settlement on a suitable substrate develops into a new sponge.

Below: **common sponges – the green form of the Breadcrumb Sponge (Halichondria panicea) mixed with orange pieces of Hymeniacidon sanguinea.**
Below right and opposite page, top: **some examples of temperate-water sponges of the class Demospongiae. Some are erect and plant-like, e.g. Axinella; Oscarella is encrusting like Cliona, which also penetrates shells. Suberites often grows on whelk shells occupied by hermit crabs.**

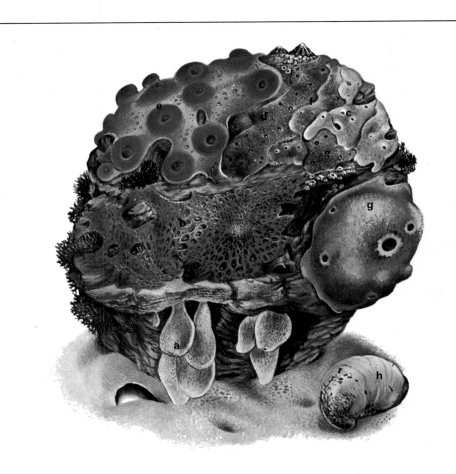

Some common species of sponges grouped on a rock surface

a *Grantia compressa* (Purse Sponge), which grows 5cm (2in) on lower shore.
b *Leucoselenia coriacea*, one of a group of closely related variable coloured species and
c *Halichondria bowerbanki*, a Breadcrumb Sponge, both 7.5-10cm (3-4in).
d *Adocia cineria* and **e** a portion of the colony at a much higher magnification.
f *Ophilitaspongia seriata*, 5cm (2in).
g *Suberites domuncula* 7.5cm (3in).
h shell of *Crepidula* (Slipper Limpet) bearing the small holes bored by the sponge *Cliona celata*

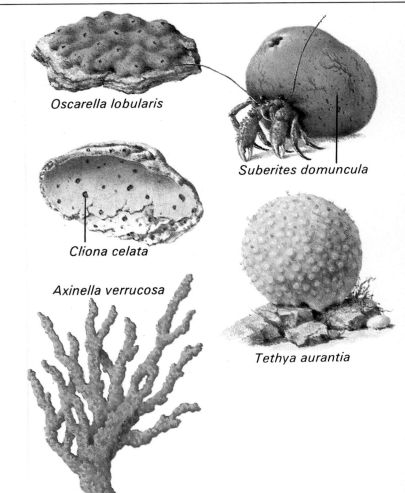

Oscarella lobularis

Suberites domuncula

Cliona celata

Axinella verrucosa

Tethya aurantia

Cnidarians

The word 'cnidaria' collectively designates these animals, and is derived from the Greek for stinging nettle, alluding to the stinging qualities of the group. Cnidarians are simple animals made up from two layers of cells separated by a layer of jelly-like material; they include some of the most beautiful of all marine animals, such as the sea-anemones and the corals. The basic body, known as the polyp, lives on the seabed or shore and is generally sac-shaped or flask-shaped. There is one opening at the top which serves as both mouth and anus. This opening is surrounded by one or more rings of tentacles, which are hollow and which enclose part of the central gut cavity of the animal. These tentacles are used in the capture of prey and in the defence of the animal, for both of which they are aided by the stinging cells. These cells are triggered by various stimuli – such as touch, or certain chemicals – and they contain a capsule called the nematocyst which discharges a thread. This thread is microscopic, but serves to penetrate or ensnare small prey, wounding and impeding it. In some types of cnidarian, such as the jellyfishes, these stinging cells are very powerful and can seriously injure a man, but in the vast majority of species they have little effect on anything but the smaller marine animals.

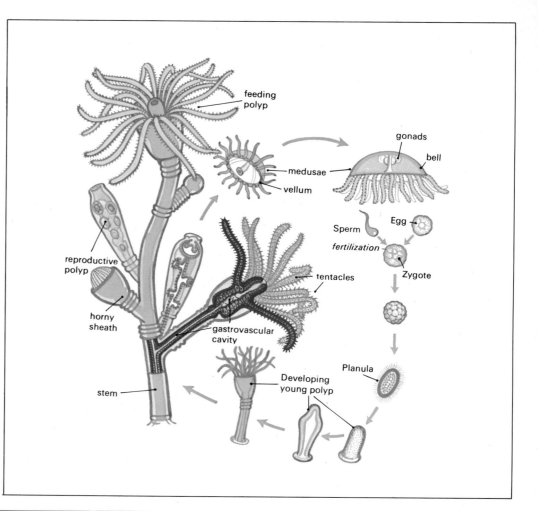

Above: **Life-cycle of a hydrozoan** *(Obelia):* **the reproductive polyps produce medusae, which release either sperms or eggs into the water. The fertilized egg is called a zygote and it develops into a larva, or 'planula', which is free-swimming until it settles on a suitable substrate to develop into a new polyp. The free-swimming stage assures distribution of the species.** *Left:* **photograph of a tubularian hydroid. The reproductive bodies are dark pink, while the feeding tentacles are pale.**

There are three main groups of cnidarian. The class Hydrozoa includes the hydroids (sometimes known as sea-firs) and some jellyfish-like organisms such as the Portuguese Man-o-War; the class Scyphozoa includes the true jellyfish, and the class Anthozoa numbers the sea-anemones, corals, soft corals, sea-fans and their allies.

There are two interesting biological features shown by the cnidaria. The first is the alternation of generations: sexual reproduction in the hydroids and jellyfishes involves two alternating life-cycle phases. Hydroid polyps produce asexually a small jellyfish, or 'medusa', which may swim free in the sea, and which bears reproductive organs. The eggs are fertilized by sperm and a larva results which swims in the sea before settling to form a new hydroid growth. In the jellyfishes the medusa stage is dominant, but the attached polyp phase follows, and lives on the sea-bed. Only in the

Corallium rubrum

Paramuricea chamaeleon

Left: gorgonians. The Red or Precious 'Coral' *(Corallium rubrum)* is often collected as a souvenir.

Physalia physalis

Velella velella

Below: the sea-anemones are solitary anthozoans. On the left, three forms of the Beadlet Anemone *(Actinia equina)*. The Gem Anemone *(Bunodactis verrucosa)* and the red form of the Beadlet Anemone are illustrated with the tentacles retracted. The photograph underneath shows the Snakelocks Anemone *(Anemone viridis)* and patches of an encrusting red seaweed.

anthozoa is this alternation of generations lacking, and polyps only are found. The second feature is the formation of colonies (i.e. many individuals sharing the same main body structure), as in some representatives of the hydrozoa and the anthozoa. Good examples are hydroids like *Obelia*, anemones like *Parazoanthus* and corals like *Cladocora*. In hydroids the development of the colonies is such that different forms of individual occur for different functions. Special polyps deal with food gathering and digestion, others with reproducing the medusae and still others with defense. Among the anthozoans no such distinction occurs and all polyps in the colony are the same.

Above: two oceanic hydrozoans, the Portuguese Man-o-War *(Physalia physalis)* and the By-the-wind Sailor *(Velella velella).* The inset shows details of the suspended polyps of the Portuguese Man-o-War.

green form

Actinia equina strawberry form

red form

Bunodactis verrucosa

Anthopleura balli 2 colour forms

Cnidarians are amongst the more common seashore animals, and it is on the rocky shore and on hard substrates in shallow water that they are seen to advantage. The oceanic hydrozoans like *Physalia*, the Portuguese Man-o-War, and *Velella*, the By-the-wind Sailor, drift far out to sea, not depending on a substrate for any of their life-cycle stages. The gas-filled float of the former and the little crescentic sail of the latter catch the air currents which cause them to drift far and wide. *Aurelia* and *Cyanea* are examples of jellyfishes more commonly found in temperate waters. The anthozoa are represented by the anemones in cooler waters, where they may be abundant. In warmer waters the reef-building corals abound.

Unsegmented worms

There are many types of worm in the animal kingdom and virtually all of these are represented in the sea. In earlier times all worms were classified together, but now zoologists identify many styles of architecture within the long narrow bodies. Each different level of organization can be related to a different life-style. The types described here are those most likely to be encountered by the beachcomber, although there are many others. The principal distinction to be made is between worms whose bodies are divided up into a number of segments, and those whose bodies are not. The former are known as segmented worms and belong to the phylum Annelida; the latter, the unsegmented worms, are distributed amongst several phyla of which two are dealt with here – phyla Platyhelminthes and Nemertina.

The simplest worms are the flatworms (phylum Platyhelminthes). As their name suggests these have flat bodies, often of leaf-like shape. There are four types of flatworm, but only the free-living turbellarians such as *Prostheceraeus* and *Thysanozoon* are likely to be encountered on the shore. These are small animals, the last mentioned being large by turbellarian standards at 5 cm in length. Most species are much smaller. They glide over the substrate by means of the combined action of thousands of cilia on their undersides, and they forage for minute prey, bacteria and scraps of carrion.

The nemertine worms represent a slightly higher level of evolution. Like the flatworms their bodies are made up of three cell layers, but whereas the flatworms have a gut opening by a mouth only, the nemertines have evolved an anus and a through gut system. They also have a rudimentary blood system and a characteristic eversible probos-

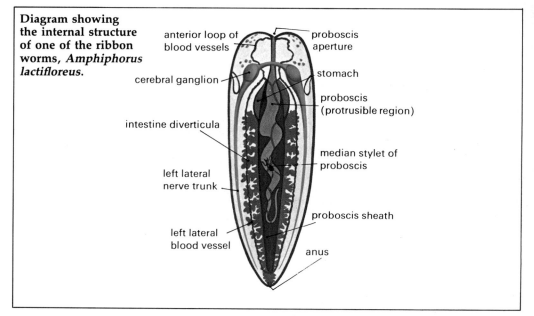

Diagram showing the internal structure of one of the ribbon worms, *Amphiphorus lactifloreus*.

anterior loop of blood vessels — proboscis aperture — cerebral ganglion — stomach — proboscis (protrusible region) — intestine diverticula — median stylet of proboscis — left lateral nerve trunk — proboscis sheath — left lateral blood vessel — anus

cis which is extended to capture prey and manipulate it into the mouth. The nemertines are all long and flat, which accounts for their common name 'ribbon worms'. Many species are fragile, often breaking up into sections when handled. The head is distinguishable at the front end, and with the aid of a hand lens minute eyespots may be seen. At either side of the head there are deep clefts, the cephalic slits, which are thought to be areas of special sensitivity. Although many species are predacious a few are

parasitic, living for example inside the mantle cavities of bivalve molluscs where they may use a sucker to maintain their position. Many ribbon worms burrow in sand and mud, and they often form an important constituent of the biota of soft shores. A smaller number, e.g. *Lineus longissimus* may be found on rocky shores. *Lineus longissimus* is a large nemertine reaching up to 1 meter or more. It is usually found on north Atlantic beaches rolled up in a mass about the size of a tennis ball.

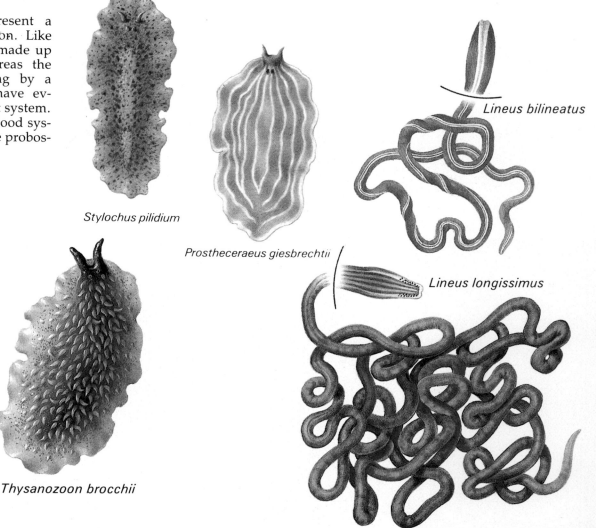

Stylochus pilidium

Prostheceraeus giesbrechtii

Lineus bilineatus

Lineus longissimus

Thysanozoon brocchii

Prostheceraeus vittatus

Segmented worms

The phylum Annelida comprises the worms whose bodies are divided up into a number of recognizable segments. There are three principal types of annelids, the bristle worms (polychaetes), the earthworms (oligochaetes) and the leeches (hirudineans). Although all three are represented in the sea, only the bristle worms are conspicuous marine animals, invading all marine habitats from the seashore to the plankton and down to the ocean abyss.

The polychaetes can be separated into two main types, known as errant and sedentary, although this division is not a very scientific one – rather it is a reflection of the two general life-styles the polychaetes pursue. As the names suggest, the former are active worms which need to move about in order to capture prey. There are many architectural styles of errant polychaetes, from short creeping worms like *Harmothoe*, whose dorsal surface is protected by scales, via active swimmers such as *Tomopteris*, with its transparent body, to massive active hunters such as *Nereis* and *Marphysa*. All these worms, though of different sizes and different general appearances, have certain features in common. These include a fairly well developed head equipped with tentacles and palps for sensory-perception, as well as eyes. The forepart of the gut frequently takes the form of an eversible proboscis which can be extended out through the mouth, and which is often equipped with jaws and teeth for subduing the prey. These jaws can give a man quite a nip, as many

sea-anglers who have handled rag-worm will testify. The segments of the body are each equipped with a pair of simple limb-like structures known as parapodia which assist with creeping, walking and swimming. Bristles are borne on the tips of the parapodia. These active worms may live among rocks, like *Eulalia*, or they burrow in sand and mud, like *Phyllodoce* or *Nephtys*.

The sedentary types have other ways of obtaining their food supply. Their heads are often reduced and bear fewer sensory structures. Some like *Arenicola* are efficient burrowers and live in U-shaped galleries in the sand. They ingest the sand, digest from it any organic material: in this respect they are rather like earthworms. A number of types form permanent tubes, either like those of *Sabella*, set in the sand, or like those of *Serpula* and *Pomatoceros*, which are chalky and which are attached to the rocks. Worms such as these carry elaborate crowns of tentacles on their heads which can be extended from the front of the tube in favourable conditions, but which can be withdrawn rapidly when danger threatens. These crowns collect particles of suspended food material from the water and pass them down to the mouth.

Most polychaetes have a life-cycle which involves a free-swimming larva. The eggs and sperm are released directly into the sea, where fertilization takes place. The larva feeds in the plankton until ready to metamorphose, at which time it descends to the seabed and becomes a juvenile worm.

Phyllodoce maculata

Eulalia viridis

Harmothoë impar

tubes

anterior of worm

Pomatoceros triqueter

Serpula vermicularis

tube anterior of worm

Left: ***Chaetopterus variopedatus,*** **a highly specialized annelid worm, secretes a parchment-like tube and pumps water through this for feeding.**

Molluscs

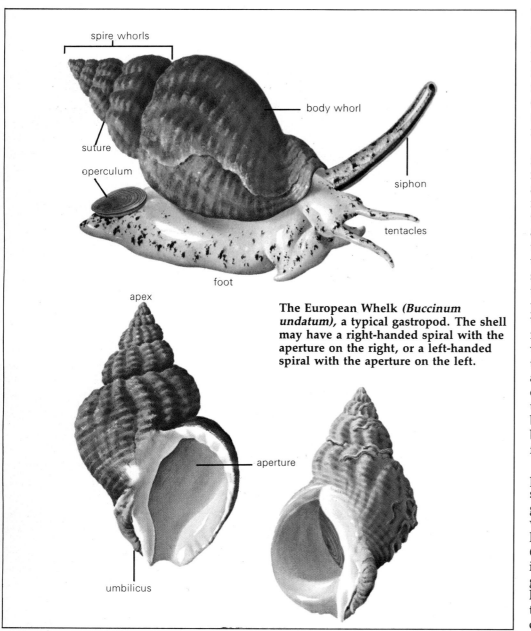

The European Whelk *(Buccinum undatum),* a typical gastropod. The shell may have a right-handed spiral with the aperture on the right, or a left-handed spiral with the aperture on the left.

The molluscs are one of the major groups of invertebrate animals, and one of the few that have successfully conquered land. However it is in the sea that we find representatives of *all* types of living molluscs, and a number of these may be encountered on the shore. Rocky and sandy shores are both good places to find molluscs.

The mollusc body is complex and difficult to describe in a general way that relates to all types. Essentially these animals have a head, a foot, an abdominal region and a flap of tissue known as the mantle. The mantle secretes the characteristic shell, a single spiral structure in the sea-snails, a pair of shells in the bivalves, and an internal structure in the squids and cuttlefishes. In most other types the shell is lacking. The shell is for protection and support and encloses the vital organs of the body, especially the mantle chamber or cavity of snails, bivalves, squids and octopuses. Here lie the gills and orifices of the reproductive and secretory tracts. Molluscs are also characterized by a horny tongue, the radula, which is especially used in the herbivorous sea-snails for scraping and browsing for food, and in the carnivores for drilling into shells and eating prey.

On the rocky shores of both the temperate and tropical regions of the world sea-snails and bivalves often occur in great numbers. On the shores of northwest Europe limpets like *Patella*, periwinkles like *Littorina* and topshells such as *Gibbula* abound. In some places it is possible to find several species of the same genus on one shore, living at different levels above the low tide mark, because they have adapted to withstand different conditions of desiccation and heat.

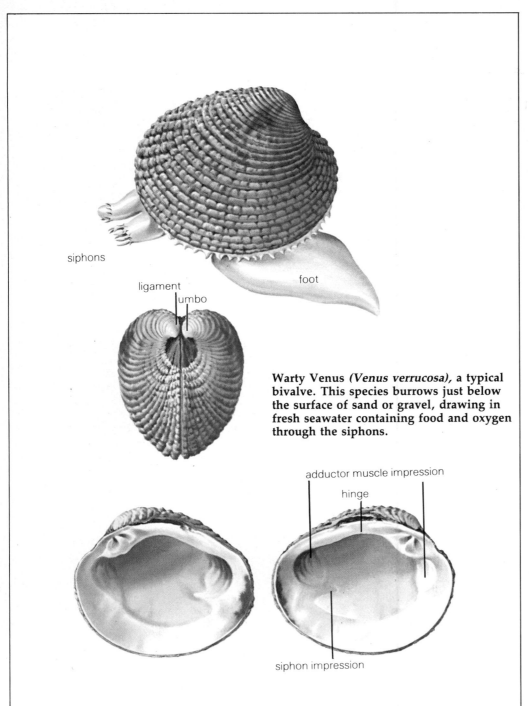

siphons

ligament

umbo

foot

Warty Venus *(Venus verrucosa),* a typical
bivalve. This species burrows just below
the surface of sand or gravel, drawing in
fresh seawater containing food and oxygen
through the siphons.

adductor muscle impression

hinge

siphon impression

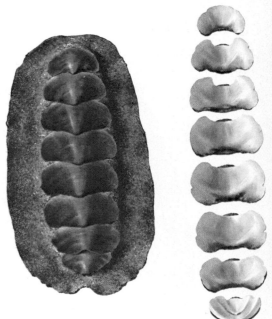

Above: A chiton, or coat-of-mail shell, in
its natural state with the fleshy girdle
(left) and with the eight plates separated.

Many shore-dwelling snails are herbivorous, browsing on the microscopic film
of algae which covers the rocks. Some
species may be adapted to feed on
lichens at the top of the shore, but very
few feed directly on the large algae. Bivalves such as the mussel *Mytilus* and
the oysters *Ostrea* and *Crassostrea* may
also be found on rocks. They are sedentary and depend on a supply of seawater
to bring them oxygen and suspended
food particles.

Sandy shores provide a burrowing
habitat for a variety of bivalves, and
although the range of species is not as
great on any one sandy shore as it is on
any one rocky shore, the density of
animals may be greater. This is because
once the burrowing habit has been evolved it opens up the way for tremen-
dous evolutionary success if sufficient

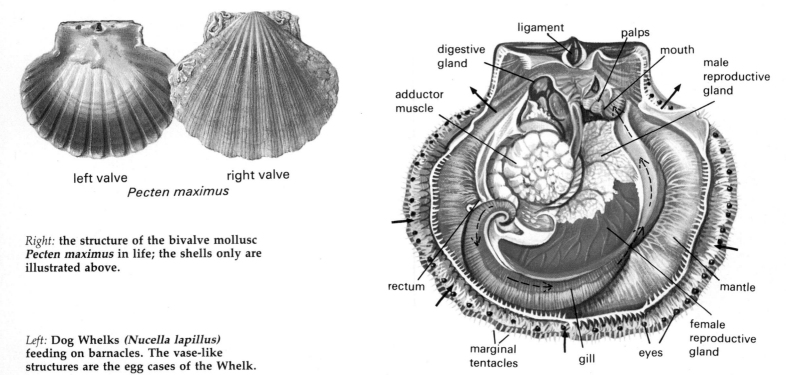

left valve

right valve

Pecten maximus

Right: the structure of the bivalve mollusc
Pecten maximus in life; the shells only are
illustrated above.

Left: Dog Whelks *(Nucella lapillus)*
feeding on barnacles. The vase-like
structures are the egg cases of the Whelk.

ligament

palps

digestive
gland

mouth

adductor
muscle

male
reproductive
gland

rectum

mantle

marginal
tentacles

gill

eyes

female
reproductive
gland

Molluscs (continued)

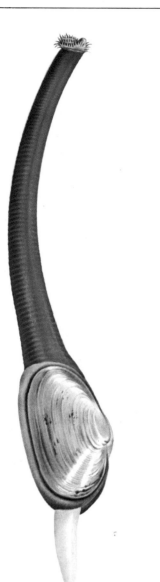

The Sand Gaper *(Mya arenaria),* which is fished commercially off the eastern coast of the USA. The long siphon is too large to fit inside the shell and is permanently extended. The burrowing foot is seen below.

Mussels attach themselves by byssus threads to rocks and stones on the shore and in shallow water. The foot enables them to move from one attachment point to another.

Above: in this photograph the well-developed foot of the tellin *(Tellina)* can be seen burrowing into the sand; the long siphons are withdrawn.

Right: nudibranchs are slug-like molluscs lacking a shell. They are often highly coloured and are among the most beautiful of marine animals.

Dendronotus frondosus

Limacia clavigera

Spurilla neapolitana

foot

byssus

syphon   gills

Facelina auriculata

Aeolidia papillosa

living space and food are available. Most burrowing bivalves are suspension feeders – the clam *Mya* and the cockle *Cerastoderma* live like this, and use extended siphons to draw water in to the mantle chamber, clear of the sand. The tellins, such as *Tellina*, are deposit-feeders, and they use their inhalent siphons to suck the layer of detritus that accumulates on the surface of the sediment. Some sea-snails are able to live successfully in or on the sand. *Natica*, the necklace shell, is an example. This burrows under the sand using its large foot and lives as a predator on other invertebrates burrowing there.

Sea-slugs are frequently amongst the most beautiful of marine invertebrates. They are sometimes brightly coloured like *Facelina* or *Limacia*. Some species are restricted to life on another organism which may serve as the sole food supply. They have evolved for errant life without protective shells. Being so brightly coloured they need some defence against predators themselves, and it has been suggested that their foul taste serves to prevent them being eaten by larger animals such as fish. The Sea-hare *Aplysia* is herbivorous and is frequently found on the beaches of northwest Europe during the summer months.

Squids and octopuses are highly mobile and may occasionally be found stranded on the shore. They represent the climax of molluscan evolution. Squids are superb swimmers and are equipped with good senses, including eyesight, and a large brain to control the complex body. They are able to change colour rapidly. Cuttle fish have evolved for life in shallow water over sandy bottoms, where they lie in wait for unwary victims which they seize with their suckered tentacles. Their camouflage renders them virtually invisible. Octopuses dwell among rocks. They can swim, but catch their prey by patience and stealth. They feed particularly on crabs, hermit crabs and other small animals, which they subdue with venomous saliva and eat with their beak-like jaws.

Below: cuttlefishes, squids and octopuses – molluscs of the class Cephalopoda. Cuttlefishes and squids have an internal shell or 'cuttlebone' which may be found washed up on the shore; the octopuses lack a shell altogether except in rare cases such as the Paper Nautilus (*Argonauta argo*).

Sepia officinalis

Sepiola rondeleti

Ptodarodes sagittatus

Loligo vulgaris

Eledone moschata

Octopus vulgaris

Argonauta argo

Below: a Toothed Winkle (*Monodonta lineata*) on barnacles; a common mollusc of the middle shore.

Nautilus scrobarius. The few species of **Nautilus** are the only cephalopods to have a true external shell.

Cone shells

Conus leopardus

Conus marmoreus

Conus imperialis

Conus litteratus

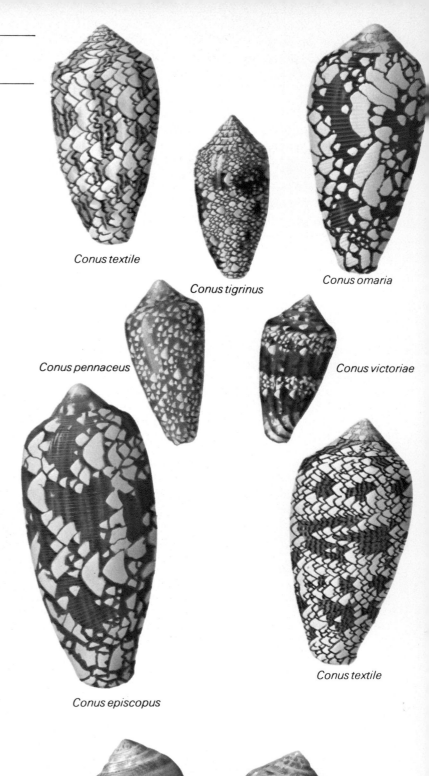

Conus textile

Conus tigrinus

Conus omaria

Conus pennaceus

Conus victoriae

Conus episcopus

Conus textile

Conus catus

Conus catus

Conus achatinus

Conus sculletti

Conus purpurascens

The Cone family (Conidae) contains shells
with an enormous variety of patterns and
colours, and for many shell collectors the
genus *Conus* is the most popular of all.
The cones are carnivores, and the sting
with which they kill their prey can be
dangerous to human beings – of ones
illustrated here, *C. marmoreus* and *C.
textile* are the most notorious. Most cones
live in tropical waters, the few that live in
subtropical waters being generally small
and less colourful. Members of the same
species can vary considerably in
appearance, as shown by the two
examples of *C. textile* illustrated here.

Cowrie shells

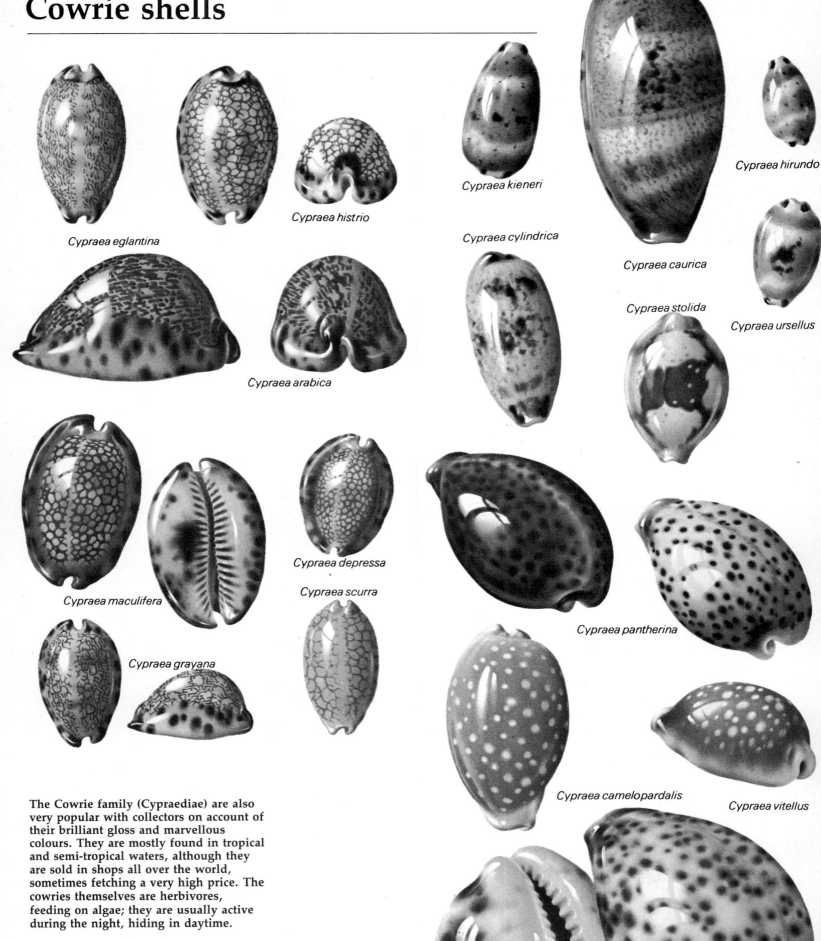

Cypraea eglantina

Cypraea histrio

Cypraea kieneri

Cypraea cylindrica

Cypraea hirundo

Cypraea caurica

Cypraea arabica

Cypraea stolida

Cypraea ursellus

Cypraea maculifera

Cypraea depressa

Cypraea scurra

Cypraea grayana

Cypraea pantherina

Cypraea cameleopardalis

Cypraea vitellus

The Cowrie family (Cypraediae) are also very popular with collectors on account of their brilliant gloss and marvellous colours. They are mostly found in tropical and semi-tropical waters, although they are sold in shops all over the world, sometimes fetching a very high price. The cowries themselves are herbivores, feeding on algae; they are usually active during the night, hiding in daytime.

Cypraea tigris

Conch shells

The conches (shells of the genus *Strombus*) are found throughout the tropics and vary widely in size. A characteristic of these shells is the 'stromboid notch', an indentation near the bottom of the outer lip through which one of a pair of tentacles, each carrying a well-developed eye, protrudes. The foot is very muscular and can turn the animal over or move it along remarkably quickly. They live in shallow water on sand or sandy mud, and are herbivorous. Some, such as the huge Queen Conch *(Strombus gigas)* – illustrated right – are prized as food, and shells may be found with a hole in the spire which was made to facilitae removal of the animal.

Strombus gigas

Strombus canarium

Strombus erythrinus rugosus

Strombus fusiformis

Strombus dentatus

Strombus pugilis

Strombus marginatus robustus

Strombus canarium form *turturella*

Strombus alatus

Strombus sinuatus

Murex shells

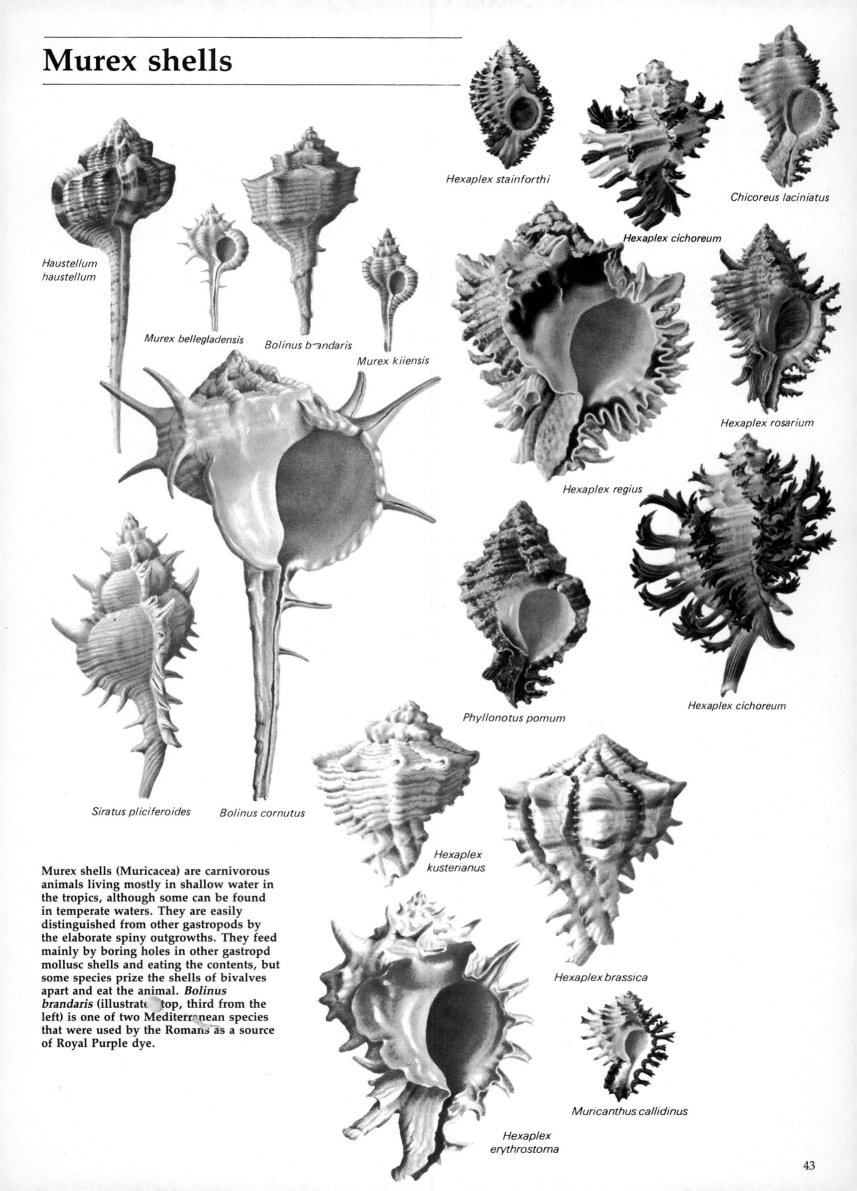

Hexaplex stainforthi

Chicoreus laciniatus

Hexaplex cichoreum

Haustellum haustellum

Murex bellegladensis

Bolinus brandaris

Murex kiiensis

Hexaplex rosarium

Hexaplex regius

Hexaplex cichoreum

Phyllonotus pomum

Siratus pliciferoides

Bolinus cornutus

Hexaplex kusterianus

Hexaplex brassica

Murex shells (Muricacea) are carnivorous animals living mostly in shallow water in the tropics, although some can be found in temperate waters. They are easily distinguished from other gastropods by the elaborate spiny outgrowths. They feed mainly by boring holes in other gastropd mollusc shells and eating the contents, but some species prize the shells of bivalves apart and eat the animal. *Bolinus brandaris* (illustrated top, third from the left) is one of two Mediterranean species that were used by the Romans as a source of Royal Purple dye.

Hexaplex erythrostoma

Muricanthus callidinus

Crustaceans

The crustaceans are a large group of aquatic animals. Their relationship with other groups of jointed limbed animals has been the subject of revised thinking recently, although for a long time they were grouped as a class within the phylum Arthropoda along with the insects, spiders etc.

The crustacean body plan is complex. There is generally a well developed head, and the rest of the body consists of a thorax and an abdomen. In some groups, however, the head and thorax may be fused into a single part of the shell known as the carapace. The bodies of these animals are segmented; each seg-

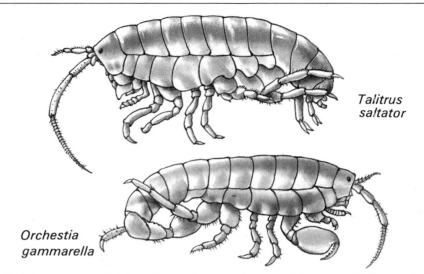

Talitrus saltator

Orchestia gammarella

Above: **sand-hoppers.** *Talitrus saltator* **inhabits the upper shore and is often associated with rotting seaweeds.** *Orchestia gamarella* **is often found among rocks and stones from the upper to middle shore.**
Left: **Sea-slaters. These crustaceans resemble terrestrial woodlice and are found on rocks above the intertidal zone.**

The most typical shore-dwelling crustaceans are the crabs, the sand hoppers and the barnacles. The crabs represent the peak of crustacean evolution. They are highly mobile and scurry about in search of food, which may be carrion or live animals. They have undergone such refinements that many are almost terrestrial. Examples of crabs that depend little on the sea, other than as a source of water to replenish their gill moisture, are the Ghost Crabs of sandy beaches in the Mediterranean and tropical Indo-west

ment bears paired jointed appendages which serve some specific function. The segments of the head contribute appendages which serve as antennae, jaws and accessory mouth parts; those of the thorax provide the walking legs which may have nippers and which may act in part as gills too, and the abdominal appendages consist of a variety of structures including gills and swimming and reproductive appendages.

Crustaceans are well represented on shores, where their hard calcareous shelly exoskeleton gives support and protection as well as helping to keep water loss to a minimum when the tide is out, and where the jointed limbs can act efficiently in food gathering and locomotion.

The body plan of the Common Lobster (*Homarus gammarus*) shows the chief features of the malacostracan crustaceans. The body consists of a combined head and thorax (cephalothorax or carapace) and an abdomen of six segments. The nippers or 'chelae' assist in the tearing of food, while the pleopods beneath the abdomen are used in both swimming and in the females for brooding eggs.

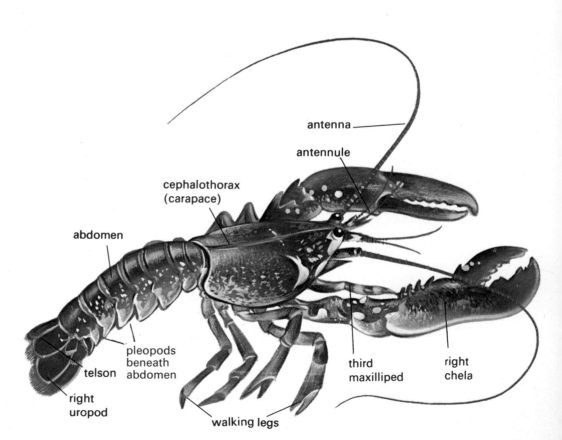

antenna

antennule

cephalothorax (carapace)

abdomen

pleopods beneath abdomen

telson

right uropod

walking legs

third maxilliped

right chela

Pacific, and the Chinese Mitten Crab which has evolved to penetrate fresh water. On temperate shores of northwest Europe the common shore crab *Carcinus maenas* and the edible crab *Cancer pagurus* may be found. Hermit crabs represent another group of crustaceans which also includes the squat lobsters and porcelain crabs. Their adaptations are at their extreme in the case of *Birgus*, the Robber Crab, which climbs trees in pursuit of food. The Hermits proper have adopted

Lepas anatifera   *Lepas fascicularis*

Above: **two pelagic (floating) species of crustacean – the Goose Barnacle (*Lepas anatifera*), which normally lives attached to boats and driftwood, and the Buoy-making Barnacle *(L. fascicularis)*, which secretes a spongy white float and is often found washed ashore after gales.**

Nephrops norvegicus

Above: **variously known as Norway Lobster, Dublin Bay Prawn or Scampi,** *Nephrops norvegicus* **is a great culinary delicacy.**
Below: **the Edible Crab** *(Cancer pagurus)* **and two other common temperate species.**

the practice of using discarded marine snail shells to protect their delicate abdomens.

The small sand hoppers with their sideways flattened bodies, and their near relatives the woodlouse-like isopods, are to be found in virtually all marine habitats. On the sandy shore the sand hoppers live amongst rotting vegetation and may burrow in the sand. On the rocky shore the sea-slaters like *Ligia* inhabit damp crevices in the shade, often near the upper limits of the tide. Most conspicuous on the rocks of the shore, however, are the barnacles, which are superbly adapted to shore life. Adult barnacles are fixed: they depend entirely for

their distribution and site selection on their free-swimming larva, the last stage of which is specialized for finding a suitable attachment point. Because they are fixed the adults do not need a head with elaborate sense organs. The head is greatly reduced and the thoracic limbs have developed to form a filter which is beaten back and forth in the sea-water to strain off minute food particles. They can only feed when covered by the tide. When the tide is out they withdraw their feeding appendages and close up the shell. The exoskeleton keeps in the water so dehydration is not a problem. If the temperature rises too much they can release a little water and keep cool.

The ghost crabs are rapid runners and inhabitants of sandy shores. They generally live in burrows and excavate sand to form a mound beside the burrow

entrance. They have large efficient eyes which can be clearly seen here. The eyes are used to warn of predators like gulls. They spend a lot of time out of water.

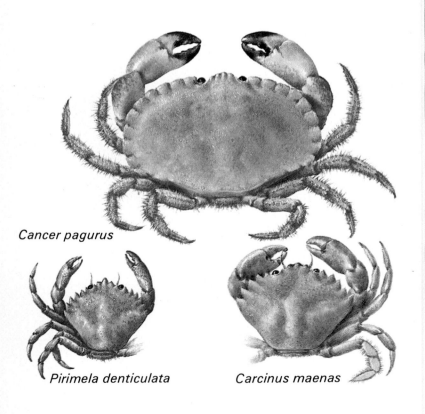

Cancer pagurus

Pirimela denticulata   *Carcinus maenas*

Starfishes, sea-urchins and other echinoderms

The echinoderms are a group of animals very distinct from all others. The name means 'spiny-skinned', and the presence of spines is a characteristic of almost all the members of the phylum. Other important characteristics of the adult include the lack of a head, the arrangement of the body in a five-sided symmetry, the possession of a unique hydraulic locomotory, feeding and respiratory apparatus known as the water-vascular system, and the peculiar internal skeleton which pushes through the outside of the body to form the spines and associated structures. The body wall is strengthened by this skeleton to form the 'test'. In most echinoderms fertilization of the eggs takes place in the sea, forming a minute planktonic larva which drifts feeding on micro-algae in the surface waters until metamorphosis takes place at settlement.

The water-vascular system is thought to have been evolved acting first as a respiratory system of protrusible hollow

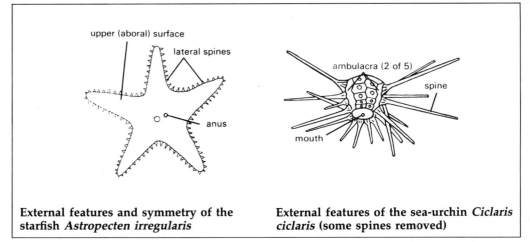

External features and symmetry of the starfish *Astropecten irregularis*

External features of the sea-urchin *Ciclaris ciclaris* (some spines removed)

tentacles, which could be withdrawn by muscles or puffed out by fluid pressure from within the body. Subsequently these tentacles become arranged around the mouth to serve in addition as food-collecting structures: this is the situation that we see in the present-day feather-stars (crinoids) such as *Antedon*. All other

modern echinoderms have 'turned over'. In the starfish, brittle-stars and sea-urchins the mouth is on the underside and the protrusible tentacles now face the substrate, but they are still arranged in rows radiating away from the mouth. These rows of 'tube-feet' are used for respiration, food gathering (in many types)

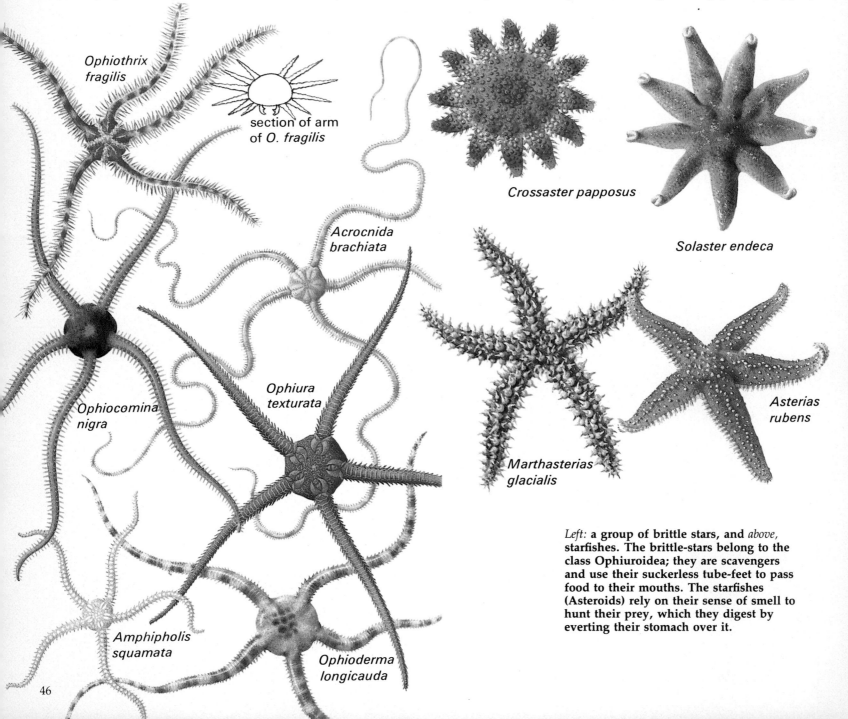

Left: **a group of brittle stars, and** *above,* **starfishes. The brittle-stars belong to the class Ophiuroidea; they are scavengers and use their suckerless tube-feet to pass food to their mouths. The starfishes (Asteroids) rely on their sense of smell to hunt their prey, which they digest by everting their stomach over it.**

and locomotion. To assist in the last mentioned role they have evolved adhesive suckers in most of the groups. Echinoderms live as suspension feeders (sea-lillies, feather stars and some sea-cucumbers), carnivores (many starfish), omnivorous browsers or pure herbivores (sea-urchins), substrate feeders (some burrowing urchins and sea-cucumbers) and predators and carrion feeders (many brittle-stars).

Echinoderms do not figure conspicuously on the seashore. However, a few species may be found on the lower shores of the world, and they abound in the shallow seas. In temperate waters the starfish such as *Asterias* and *Marthasterias* may be conspicuous predators on the shellfish beds of mussels and oysters. The larger and beautiful sun-stars also prey on bivalves and on the other starfish. *Crossaster* is a sun-star that is found in the northern waters of all our oceans. Small starfish such as *Asterina* are to be found on rocky shores all over the world. The brittle-stars are also cosmopolitan. One species, *Amphipolis squamata*, is frequently found among rocks, pebbles and weeds. Brittle-stars are conspicuous on both soft sandy and more gravelly seabeds, where they may occur in immense numbers. Small sea-urchins such as *Psammechinus* and *Paracentrotus* are common on the lower shores and in shallow water of the North Atlantic and Mediterranean. Here they browse on encrusting plants and animals, using their specially adapted teeth which are set in a complex apparatus around the mouth.

Some of the sea-urchins, heart urchins and sand-dollars have developed for life

under the sand. Although they may be difficult to find, their skeletons wash ashore in great numbers on certain sandy beaches. The sea-cucumbers are best seen on the sandy bottoms around coral reefs and in the tropics, where they occur in great numbers. Species of *Holothuria* and *Stichopus* occur widely in the Atlantic and Indo-west Pacific Oceans. Members of the genera *Synapta* and *Leptosynapta* burrow in sand and mud.

Above: a shallow water sea-cucumber, **Cucumaria normani,** an echinoderm with a very different body from those of sea-urchins, heart-urchins and sand-dollars.

Below: Sea-urchins, sand-dollars and heart-urchins. Sea-urchins like *Echinus* are globular echinoderms with a rigid shell-like test of chalky plates; they usually live on rocks and hard surfaces. Sand-dollars like *Echinocyamus* are flat, coin-like, bilaterally symmetrical burrowers. Heart-urchins like *Spatangus* also live in sand and gravel.

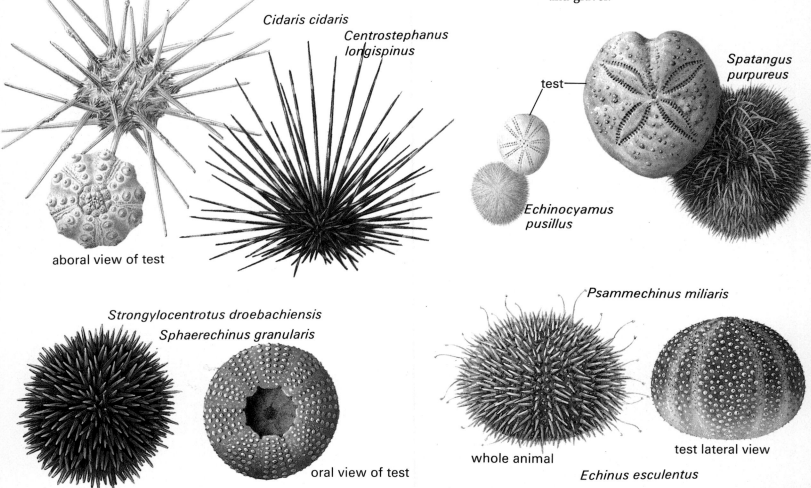

Cidaris cidaris

Centrostephanus longispinus

aboral view of test

test

Spatangus purpureus

Echinocyamus pusillus

Strongylocentrotus droebachiensis
Sphaerechinus granularis

oral view of test

Psammechinus miliaris

whole animal

test lateral view

Echinus esculentus

Bryozoans and sea-squirts

Bryozoans are sometimes known as 'moss animals'. Some species can encrust rocks and large algae, giving them a furry appearance. Although small, the animals are complex. Marine bryozoans exist as colonies – as many similar individuals sharing one body mass. In some species there are individuals specialized for different tasks, e.g. feeding and defence of the colony. The basic animal lives in a box-like skeleton which may be horny or stiffened with calcium carbonate. It cannot move about, so it is dependent on the metamorphosing bryozoan larva finding a suitable site for life as an adult. Once the larva has settled, further movement is impossible. After metamorphosis the box-like structure develops with the animal inside it. This has a mouth on the upper side surrounded by retractable tentacles; the mouth leads into a looped gut, and the anus opens on the top, outside the ring of tentacles. There is no head and there are no appendages, although the box is sometimes armed with spikes and ornaments. The tentacles form the lophophore and are covered with beating cilia. The cilia pump water into the lophophore, so extracting oxygen and collecting suspended food particles. Many species grow like *Membranipora*, an encrusting growth found on large algae; others like *Bugula* and *Cellaria* form branching growths rising up from the seabed or hanging down from overhangs. This way they require less space for attachment and can get their suspension-feeding lophophores into regions of stronger current movements.

After fertilization of the egg a planktonic larva is generally formed. This

Below: **encrusting bryozoans, often called sea-mats. The branching type is *Scrupocellaria scruposa* and the white encrusting type is *Electra pilosa*. Bryozoans are among the commonest animals inhabiting stony and rocky shores and seabeds but they are often neglected, probably on account of their small size and lack of commercial value.**

Right: **diagram showing the structure of a typical bryozoan individual within a colony; the illustrations of named species below show the whole colony in each case together with a detail of the individuals.**

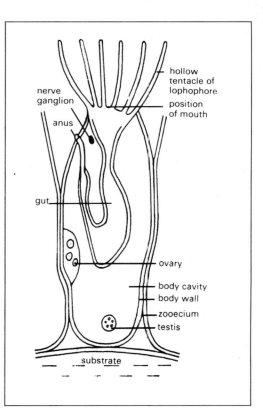

Cellaria salicornioides

Bugula neritina

Pentapora fascialis

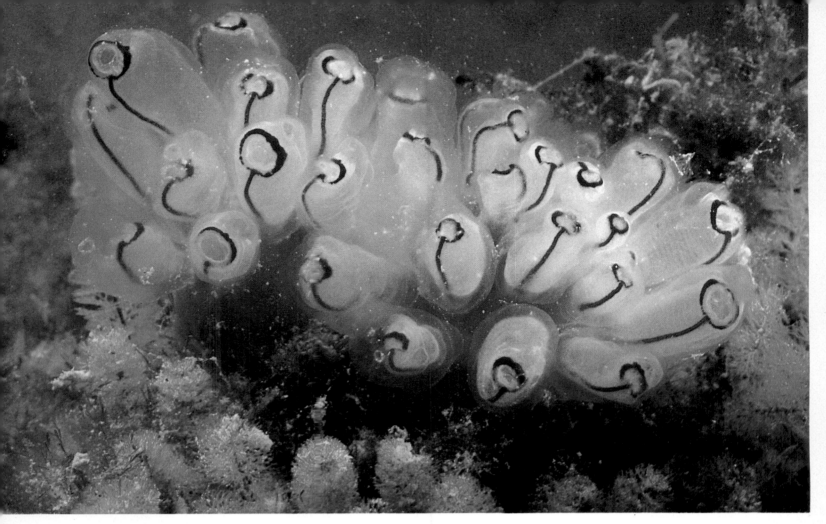

Above: **a tightly packed group of colonial sea-squirts.**

Below right: **sea-squirts (Ascidians) occur in a variety of forms. Many of the larger types are solitary, while some of the smaller ones such as the Star Ascidian (Botryllus schlosseri) are colonial and encrusting.**

serves as a distributional phase as well as a developmental one. The larval life ends at metamorphosis.

Sea-squirts, like bryozoans, are sedentary and encrusting. Many, like *Ciona* and *Styela*, are solitary. Some species are colonial, e.g. forms of *Diazona* and *Botryllus*.

The basic structure is a headless sac-like body with two openings. The larger terminal opening is the inhalent one, and down one side is the smaller exhalent opening. Seawater is drawn in through the former and passed through a relatively large barrel-shaped pharynx of many fine-meshed gill-bars. It is passed out between these bars into a sleeve-like atrium, which discharges through the exhalent opening. Waste water and faecal matter are discharged in this way. The gullet leads from the pharynx to the looped gut, and the animal feeds on suspended particles which the gills filter out. They also extract oxygen which is picked up by the rudimentary blood system and distributed throughout the body.

The outer casing of the sea-squirt is referred to as the tunic. It is unusual in the animal kingdom because it contains cellulose, a substance infrequently found in animals. The sex organs produce gametes, which are flushed out with the

waste from the atrium. Fertilization occurs in the sea and a small tadpole-like larva rapidly develops. This is free-living and acts as a distributive phase, but metamorphosis follows quickly, often in a matter of hours, when the tadpole attaches and turns into a juvenile sea-

squirt. The larva is clearly a chordate, with a rudimentary head and stiffening skeletal rod foreshadowing the development of a vertebral column. Although the adults lack such features the larval characteristics indicate that the sea-squirts are related to the vertebrates.

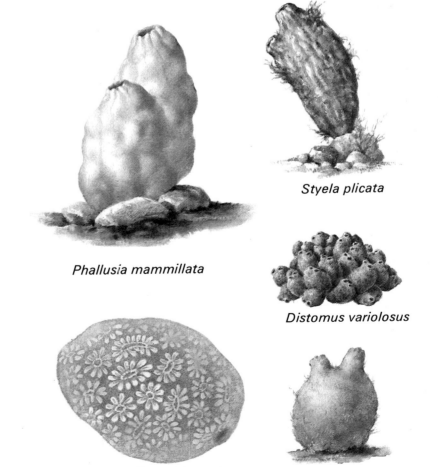

Phallusia mammillata

Styela plicata

Distomus variolosus

Botryllus schlosseri

Molgula manhattensis

Fishes

More than any other group of animals fish epitomize life in water, and in particular seawater. This is because of their abundance and wide distribution. Fish are of great commercial importance too, so their distribution, behaviour and cultivation has been of great interest to man. Marine fishes have evolved to occupy all habitats in the sea; they are abundant in the surface waters of the shallow seas, they swarm around tropical reefs and they are present in great numbers in the depths of the oceans. A few species have even become adapted for life on the shore.

The sea provides an environment for all types of fish from the lowly lampreys and hagfishes, through the sharks, skates and rays to the bony fish like eels, herrings, cods, bass, gobies and blennies. By their very nature, none of these can be true shore-dwellers in the sense that they can live for long periods exposed to air and wind, although a few types, such as the tree-climbing fish of mangrove swamps, and the mud skippers can exist for relatively long periods in the air. On temperate shores, particularly among the rocks, in crevices and in pools, many small fish may be encountered. These will include the young of sea-going species as well as adults of 'little' fish such as gobies, blennies and sucker fish. On tropical rocky shores the heat can be intense and the fishes are restricted to life in pools. Here gobies,

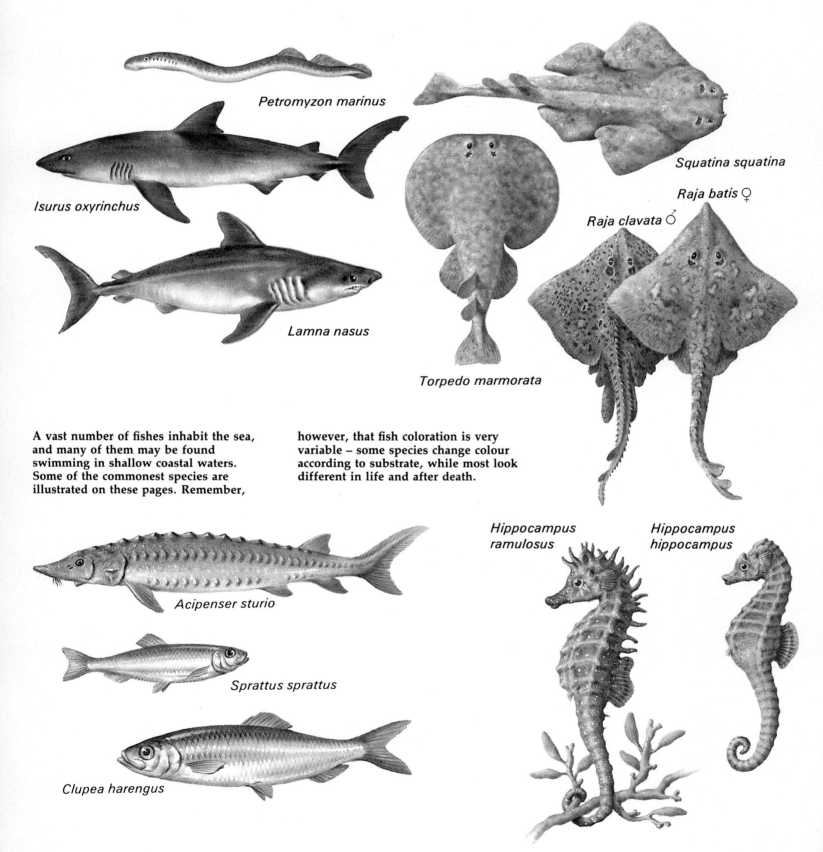

Petromyzon marinus

Isurus oxyrinchus

Lamna nasus

Torpedo marmorata

Squatina squatina

Raja batis ♀

Raja clavata ♂

A vast number of fishes inhabit the sea, and many of them may be found swimming in shallow coastal waters. Some of the commonest species are illustrated on these pages. Remember, however, that fish coloration is very variable – some species change colour according to substrate, while most look different in life and after death.

Acipenser sturio

Sprattus sprattus

Clupea harengus

Hippocampus ramulosus

Hippocampus hippocampus

blennies and pipe-fish will be found.

In the tropics, particularly in coral reef areas, the seas teem with fishes that have evolved amid intense competition for food and living space. Lagoons have been identified as important places for breeding shellfish, and it is now realized that they serve as nurseries for species which as adults live out their lives in the open sea. In parts of the world like East Africa lagoons are important places for fishing, and traps may be constructed there to catch the fish which move in with the tide to feed.

Fish are diverse not only in their form and structure, but also in their physiology and behaviour. Adaptations in-clude buoyancy mechanisms, special vision for twilight zones in the ocean depths, colour changes for camouflage or breeding purposes, sex change mechanisms, brooding behaviour and mimicry.

In assessing the importance of fish on the seashore one should not merely think in terms of the few fish that may be found there at low tide. So far as their influence on other organisms is concerned it must be remembered that many fish move into the shore area when it is flooded at high tide. They do so principally to feed, either on the plant life there, or on the range of invertebrates which emerge from cover when immersed. Because of this fish can exert considerable pressure on the development of shore communities.

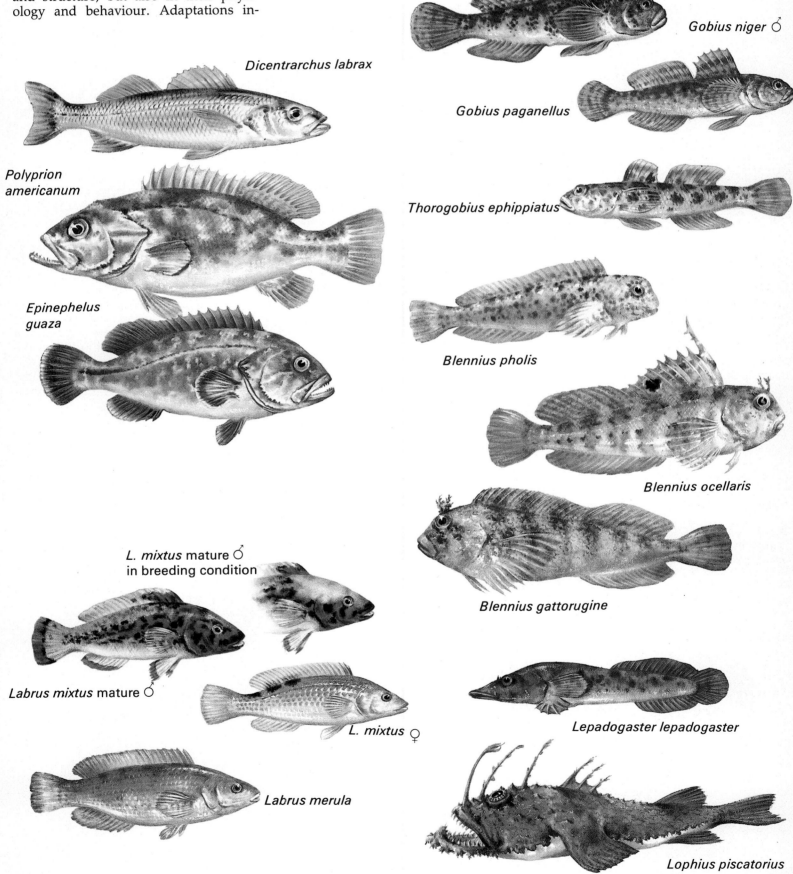

Gobius niger ♂

Dicentrarchus labrax

Gobius paganellus

Polyprion
americanum

Thorogobius ephippiatus

Epinephelus
guaza

Blennius pholis

Blennius ocellaris

Blennius gattorugine

L. mixtus mature ♂
in breeding condition

Labrus mixtus mature ♂

L. mixtus ♀

Lepadogaster lepadogaster

Labrus merula

Lophius piscatorius

Seabirds

Two species of penguin, Chinstrap (*Pygoscelis antarctica*) and Gentoo (*Pygoscelis papua*).

Frigatebirds are one of the most aerial of seabirds and are persistent pirates, forcing food from other birds. This is a displaying Magnificent Frigatebird (*Fregata magnificens*) with his gular pouch inflated.

The term seabird is usually applied to those birds which rely on the oceans' resources for most of their food. This generally restricts those birds that can be called seabirds to only four major groups: the penguins; the albatrosses, petrels and related species; the gannets, pelicans and cormorants; and finally the skuas, gulls, terns and auks. Although these groups cover only approximately three per cent of the world's 8,600 species some seabirds have enormous populations numbering many millions of individuals – Wilson's Petrel, for example is considered by some to be the most numerous bird in the world.

The penguins are found principally in the southern seas where some species form huge colonies or rookeries on the remote wind-swept islands. The Emperor Penguin has an extraordinary breeding cycle that entails the male incubating a single egg through the polar winter on the Antarctic mainland. They do this in order that the chick can take full advantage of the short summer.

The albatrosses are also largely restricted to the southern oceans where they glide effortlessly for days on their long wings travelling great distances in an almost continuous migration. They breed in colonies on remote islands.

The shearwaters and petrels are a widespread group of seabirds which, as well as including some of the most abundant species, also include some of the rarest and smallest. The shearwaters have been studied in great detail and like many seabirds have shown themselves to be expert navigators, being able to migrate precisely over thousands of miles of apparently featureless ocean.

The Pelecaniformes comprise a highly diverse group, from the frigatebirds, the 'pirates' of the seas, to the gannets – a spectacular group that has mastered the art of plunge-diving after fish.

The gulls and terns are probably the most familiar seabirds. The gulls in particular, have been highly successful in exploiting man's excesses and can often be found in great numbers scavenging around fishing ports and city harbours. The auks are restricted to the colder seas of the northern hemisphere where they often form noisy cliff nesting colonies on remote stretches of coast.

The chick of the Xantu's Murrelet (*Endomychura hypolenca*) goes to sea with its parents at a very early stage and is already equipped with enormous webbed feet.

The chick of the Puffin (*Fratercula arctica*) stays below ground in a burrow until it is fully fledged.

Cormorants are expert divers and have been found caught in fishing nets at depths of thirty metres. These are Common Cormorants (*Phalacrocorax carbo*) in full breeding plumage.

The Great Skua shown here is chasing a Kittiwake in an attempt to get it to disgorge its meal – it is also a determined predator frequently taking young chicks and eggs of other species.

Above: three typical fulmar petrels in flight – the large Giant Petrel (*Macronectes giganteus*) with a wingspan of 2 metres, the Cape Pigeon (*Daption capensis*) and the Antarctic Fulmar (*Fulmarus glacialoides*).

Below: boobies and gannets are found throughout the world's oceans. The Peruvian Booby (*Sula variegata*) breeds in huge colonies on islands off Peru and, together with the Guanay Cormorant, is one of the main guano producers. Hundreds of thousands of tons of guano – the accumulated droppings – were exported as fertilizer in the nineteenth century; this 'crop' is still exploited on a smaller scale today.

Right: gulls are highly adaptable feeders taking advantage of a wide range of food sources, particularly offal thrown overboard by fishermen, and in some areas they can become a serious nuisance at city rubbish dumps.

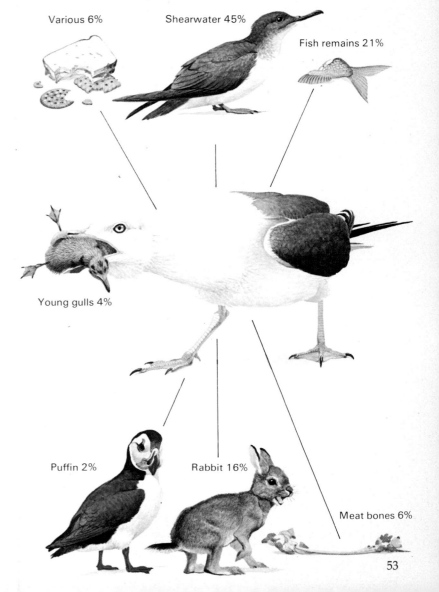

Food of Great Black-backed Gull

Various 6%   Shearwater 45%   Fish remains 21%

Young gulls 4%

Puffin 2%   Rabbit 16%   Meat bones 6%

Temperate rocky shores

A rocky shore can be divided up into three zones, according to the plants and animals that may be found there. The **upper shore** is generally populated by lichens such as *Xanthoria*, *Caloplaca* and *Ochrolechia* species. These merge almost imperceptibly with the terrestrial lichens of the rocks above. They support a population of small snails (*Littorina neritoides*) if the shore is sufficiently exposed. This snail, whilst being found at all levels of the exposed rocky shore, is the only one which can tolerate conditions at the top of the shore where it hides in crevices. The Sea-slater *Ligia oceanica*, a relative of the woodlouse, may be found hiding in shade to avoid desiccation.

The algae of the upper shore depend on the profile and exposure level. Upper shore pools frequently contain fronds of large green algae such as *Ulva*, the Sea-lettuce. Long tubular fronds of green *Enteromorpha* overlie the rocks, especially if there are freshwater runnels. The Channelled Wrack, *Pelvetia canaliculata*, is a small brown alga which forms conspicuous bands on the upper shore.

Unlike the green algae of the upper shore, which have to live in moist conditions, this alga can withstand a considerable amount of desiccation, and may dry out to a crisp black mass before the tide returns to cover it. On sheltered shores *Ascophyllum nodosum* and *Fucus*

Right: **some of the winkles that can occur in enormous numbers on a rocky shore.**

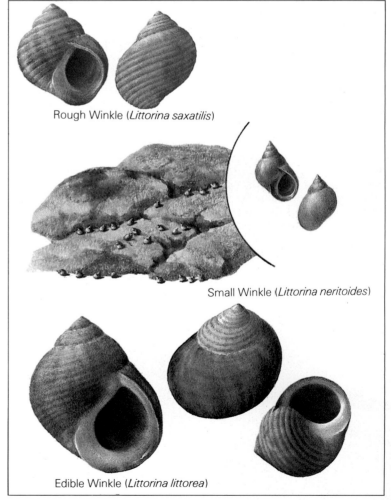

Rough Winkle (*Littorina saxatilis*)

Small Winkle (*Littorina neritoides*)

Edible Winkle (*Littorina littorea*)

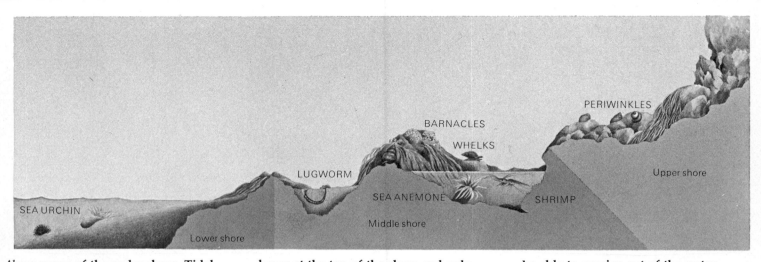

PERIWINKLES

BARNACLES

WHELKS

Upper shore

LUGWORM

SEA ANEMONE

SHRIMP

SEA URCHIN

Middle shore

Lower shore

Above: **zones of the rocky shore. Tidal movements uncover the shore twice daily for a variable period which may be many** hours at the top of the shore and only minutes at the bottom, depending on the season. Exposed plants and animals must be able to survive out of the water, sometimes under hot sun or in extreme cold.

Left: **at a superficial glance the rocky shore may sometimes seem barren, but it provides a great range of habitats for plants and animals and is an ideal place to examine their zonation, which reveals a wealth of information about their ability to survive and compete.**

spiralis may occur too, covering the rocks with a thick lush layer of weed.

The **middle shore** is marked by the appearance of barnacles. About seven species of barnacle may be found, but one shore will rarely have all types because some are relatively restricted by physical conditions: *Balanus improvisus*, for example, likes the brackish waters of estuaries and lagoons. Two species of the warm water barnacle *Chthamalus* may be found in the waters of the Atlantic and the Channel around Spain, France and England, as well as in the southern North Sea. These can tolerate some heat and some desiccation, so they occur well up from the low tide level. The colder water barnacle *Semibalanus balanoides* occupies the rocks below *Chthamalus* in the south, but further north, where it is too cold for *Chthamalus*, it is the only barnacle found at this level. The Dog Whelk, *Nucella lapillus* is a predator of these barnacles and often found among them together with its egg masses. Limpets and periwinkles are also common on the middle shore. They graze on the microscopic film of algae covering the rocks. *Patella vulgata*, the Common Limpet, is one of three species that may be found on the rocky shore. The rough periwinkle, *Littorina saxatilis*, is now thought to comprise an aggregation of closely related species. It is well adapted to life on the upper and middle shore, where it may be found creeping on the rocks in search of micro-algae, or sheltering in crevices where the humidity is slightly greater than in the open. Living beside and below it is the edible periwinkle, *Littorina littorea*, which is larger, with a smoother shell. Two topshells, *Monodonta lineata* and *Gibbula umbilicalis* live at this level: all these shells contain herbivorous snails.

Above: **lichens at the top of a rocky shore. These live as dual plants, partly composed of algal tissue and partly of fungal tissue.**

Below: **mussels, barnacles, limpets and two much abraded topshells compete for space on a rocky shore.**

The algae of the middle shore are predominantly brown. The Serrated Wrack and the Bladder Wrack, *Fucus serratus* and *Fucus vesiculosus* are characteristic. The dichotomously branching fronds of both these species are flat with a midrib, and their slimy surfaces protect against abrasion as they wash back and forth over the rocks, as well as helping to reduce water loss when they are exposed to the air. The air bladders of *Fucus vesiculosus* give it buoyancy in the water. The smooth-shelled flat periwinkles, *Littorina obtusata*, live among the fronds of this alga and it has been suggested that the shape of their shells resembles that of the bladders thus distracting predators such as sea-birds. Some rock faces in this region are covered with a felty growth of small red algae called *Laurencia pinnatifida*, sometimes also known as Pepper Dulse. Other species of *Laurencia* grow in similar positions on tropical rocky shores. The fine threadlike filaments of *Ectocarpus* and *Spongonema* may coat the rocks with their slippery textured gelatinous fronds.

The **lower shore** provides a habitat for the greatest diversity of plants and animals. On many beaches the Common Mussel, *Mytilus edulis*, forms extensive beds; in some cases it extends up to part of the middle shore. Lower shore barnacles are found: *Balanus perforatus* is larger than other barnacles, reaching

30mm across and having purplish or brownish plates instead of chalky white ones. The small hydroids like *Obelia* and *Sertularia* and the larger sea-anemones *Actinia equina* and *Anemonia sulcata* wait for unwary victims to stumble into their deadly stinging tentacles. In shaded areas, sponges and sea-squirts encrust the sides of crevices, grottos and the

The Bladder Wrack *(Fucus vesiculosus)* is a common inhabitant of the temperate rocky shore.

A Purple Topshell *(Gibbula umbilicalis)* with barnacles on the middle shore.

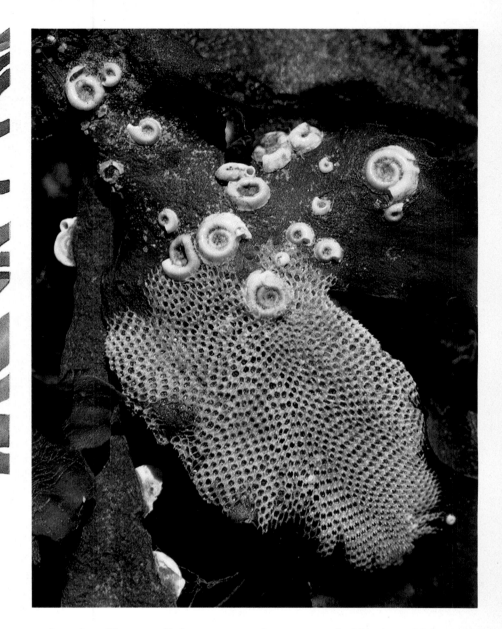

Above: **sea-mat and Spirorbis borealis (a tube-dwelling polychaete worm) on the Toothed Wrack (Fucus serratus).**

Laminaria hyperborea

Saccorhiza polyschides

Above: **two kelps of the family Laminariaceae, which includes some of the largest algae found in European waters.**

Left: **the Beadlet Anemone (Actinia equina) is common on rocks and in crevices down to about 8 metres.**

overhangs of rocks. The small lower shore topshell *Gibbula cineraria* feeds on microscopic films of algae, and lives among small rocks, shells and the holdfasts of algae. More specialist mollusc feeders may also be encountered here. The little European Cowrie, *Trivia monacha*, feeds on colonies of sea-squirts, and the sponges are preyed upon by certain sea-slugs, e.g. *Archidoris*, which come ashore in the spring and summer months to spawn, laying ther eggs in curly ribbons on the rocks. Rocks may be encrusted with colonies of bryozoans such as *Electra* and with the chalky tubes of the serpulid worms *Pomatoceros* and *Spirorbis*. These animals are suspension feeders, and they in turn provide food for omnivorous browsers such as the green sea-urchin *Psammechinus*. The starfish *Asterias* and *Marthasterias* are efficient predators, moving around when covered by the tide to feed on bivalves such as mussels and oysters. A number of small fish such as gobies, blennies, the Cornish Sucker and Butterfish may be found in the rock pools of the lower shore, or even stranded under stones and weeds, where so long as they keep damp they are able to survive until the tide returns.

The large algae of the lower shore are frequently its most conspicuous organisms. The kelps such as *Laminaria* are brown algae incapable of surviving much desiccation, and they do not occur on very exposed shores. Dabberlocks, *Alaria esculenta*, is characteristic of exposed places, as is *Himanthalia elongata*. At this level there are many red algae, giving the rocks and the insides of pools a pink-red hue. *Chondrus crispus*, *Gigartina stellata*, *Corallina officinalis* and *Palmaria palmata* are all typical.

Temperate sandy shores

After viewing the rocky shore at low tide the sandy shore seems barren. There is no lush growth of macro-algae, and apart from sea-grasses there is no obvious plant life, unless the odd rock or pebble allows a plant suitable attachment. Few animals live on the surface, so the explorer has to look for telltale signs of life below the sand, such as tube openings and burrow mouths. Most organisms colonizing the sand live *in* it rather than *on* it. This creates a need for a suitable burrowing mechanism, which may take the form of the proboscis and parapodia of polychaete worms such as the lugworm *Arenicola* and the catworm *Nephtys*, or the foot of shore-dwelling bivalve molluscs like the Striped Venus Shell *Venus striatula* and the Otter-shell *Lutraria lutraria*. The bivalve body is particularly well suited to burrowing because it is entirely enclosed in a streamlined shell. This style of life is epitomized by the narrow razor shells such as *Ensis*, where the foot is relatively large and powerful and can pull the shell below the surface very quickly. Other animals that have evolved for life in sand are the burrowing starfish *Astropecten* and the burrowing brittle-star *Ophiura*. Sea-cucumbers like *Synapta* and

The segmented worms are abundant on sandy shores all over the world. The

Lugworm *(Arenicola marina)* is often used as a bait by sea-anglers.

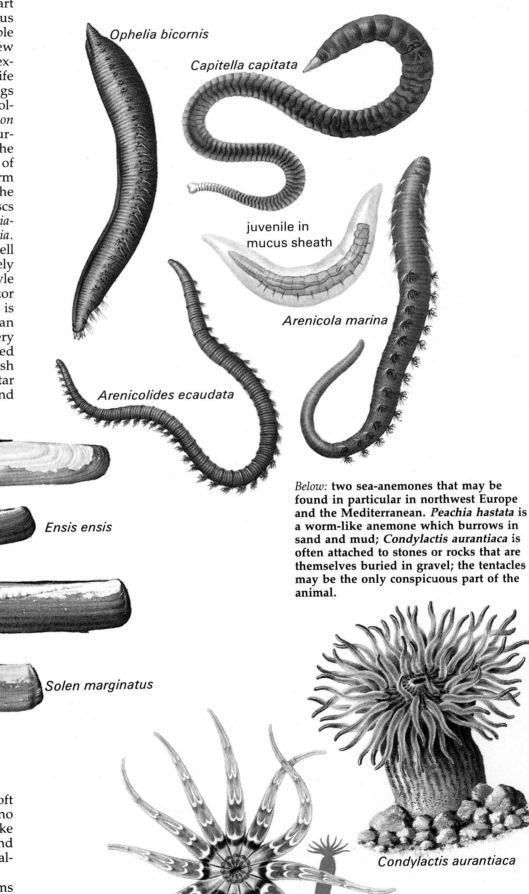

Ophelia bicornis

Capitella capitata

juvenile in mucus sheath

Arenicola marina

Arenicolides ecaudata

Pharus legumen

Ensis ensis

Ensis siliqua

Solen marginatus

Above: the Razor Shells are well adapted for burrowing in sand. Some of them burrow down as fast as a shell collector can dig.

anemones like *Peachia* employ their soft bodies to burrow, but they have no special burrowing appendages, unlike the burrowing sea-urchins *Spatangus* and *Echinocardium* with their highly specialized spines and tube-feet.

Burrowing is only one of the problems that have to be overcome before life in the sand can be established. Once in position under the sand a stream of fresh oxygen-bearing seawater has to be supplied to the gills. In polychaetes like the lugworm this water is pumped through the burrows by peristaltic activity of the

Below: two sea-anemones that may be found in particular in northwest Europe and the Mediterranean. *Peachia hastata* is a worm-like anemone which burrows in sand and mud; *Condylactis aurantiaca* is often attached to stones or rocks that are themselves buried in gravel; the tentacles may be the only conspicuous part of the animal.

Condylactis aurantiaca

whole animal

Peachia hastata

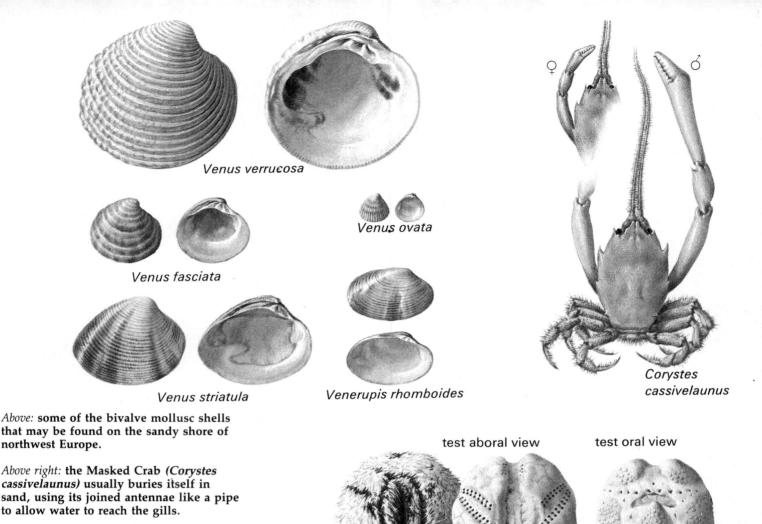

Venus verrucosa

Venus fasciata

Venus ovata

Venus striatula

Venerupis rhomboides

Corystes
cassivelaunus

Above: **some of the bivalve mollusc shells that may be found on the sandy shore of northwest Europe.**

Above right: **the Masked Crab** *(Corystes cassivelaunus)* **usually buries itself in sand, using its joined antennae like a pipe to allow water to reach the gills.**

test aboral view   test oral view

Echinocardium cordatum

Above: **the Sea-potato** *(Echinocardium cordatum),* **an echinoderm – the illustrations show the whole animal and the test alone, seen from above (the aboral view) and below (oral view).**

Below: **one of the Brittle-stars** *(Acrocnida brachiata).* **This species burrows in sand but one or two of the arms reach up to the surface to maintain a supply of oxygen-bearing water.**

body wall. Others such as *Lanice, Amphitrite* and *Sabella* extend out from their burrows, withdrawing if danger threatens. In the cases of the bivalve molluscs the body wall is extended to form two siphons, one bringing clean water to the gills and one carrying oxygen-depleted water away from them. This system combines well with filter feeding, as the inhalent water stream carries food particles which can be sieved by the gills. Other animals feed by ingesting the substrate and digesting any suitable organic material. Still others, such as *Astropecten,* are efficient predators, detecting their prey at a distance by smell and moving swiftly over the surface to engulf it; they may also capture by burrowing.

Some animals do not burrow completely. The Common Shrimp nestles in the ripple marks of the sand and scavenges for carrion. Various crabs live on the surface and one, *Corystes,* is able to live a fully burrowing life: it uses its two antennae like a snorkel to draw water below the sand for respiration. The cuttle-fish *Sepia* is one of the larger predators of the sandy shore, moving in at high water to prey on small fish. It has astonishing powers of camouflage and can adjust its coloration to match the background.

Zonation of organisms occurs on the sandy shore as well as on the rocky shore, but the effects of the ebb and flow of the tides are less marked below the sand. The sun does not warm up the sand 10 centimeters deep as much as on the surface, and water is not completely drained from between the sand grains, so the risks of desiccation and overheating are less at low water.

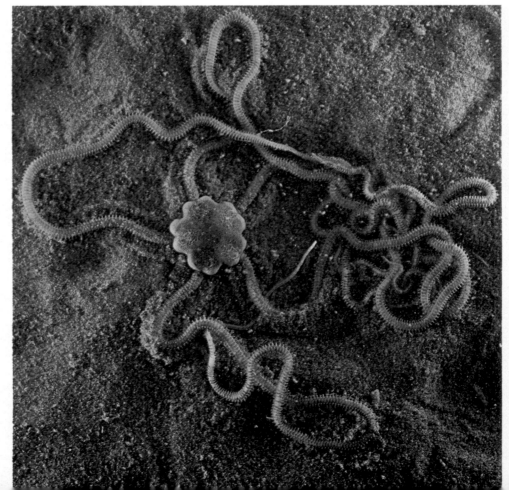

Temperate muddy shores and estuaries

At first sight the muddy shore and the estuary may seem the least attractive of our shore types. Frequently these habitats are either dirty in appearance or have been despoiled by bad planning and industrial developments. The two are often connected, since the mud consists of very small particles of sediment carried to the sea by rivers. When the river flow slows as it nears the sea, the particles sediment out and accumulate as mud banks or spits, as well as lining the shore. Mud accumulates in sheltered areas, and in exposed regions it is swept away. Because of the freshwater input from the

river and the marine influence of the sea, many such habitats have water of fluctuating salinity throughout the tidal cycle. Despite the disadvantages of variable salinity and the risk of fine particles clogging internal structures such as gills, as well as lack of firm substrates like the rock, muddy shores and estuaries are usually very productive habitats – as long as the mud is stable it may support many organisms. As with the sandy shore, there is not a diverse flora and fauna; rather, diversity is low in terms of species, but density of organisms is high, since if a species surves on this type of

Estuaries are broad stretches of water where rivers and oceans meet. They may be rich in plant and animal life, but in industrial countries they are often busy with shipping and heavily polluted by oil and factory wastes.

Below left: the Blunt Gaper *(Mya truncata)* and the Sand Gaper *(M. arenaria)* may both be found burrowing in the mud of estuaries.

Below: Glasswort *(Salicornia europaea).* With its long root this plant has an important role in colonizing bare mud.

right valve

left valve

posterior view

Mya truncata

Mya arenaria left valve

shore there is likely to be plenty of food for it.

The productivity of estuaries and muddy shores depends on the land and its drainage. Mineral salts, leached from the soil by rainfall, are transported in solution to the estuaries where they are available for photosynthesis. The algae that benefit most are the minute members of the phytoplankton drifting in the surface waters where light is plentiful. Even if larger plants were able to gain a holding point, they would be shielded from good illumination when covered by water because of its turbidity. This turbidity is largely due to particles of silt, but detritus (dead organic material) will be there too, and this forms an important element in the food supply of many animals. Thus filter-feeders are numerous, whether they feed on algae or detritus. Examples of polychaetes and bivalve molluscs which do this are especially numerous. Once the primary converters of plant to animal material are established, the carnivorous animals will always succeed. Typical muddy shore and estuarine polychaetes are *Nereis diversicolor*, which feeds on other worms, and *Sabella pavonina* and *Myxicola infundibulum*, both of which filter particles from the water. Bivalves such as the cockle *Cerastoderma edule* and the clam *Mya arenaria* may occur in great numbers, and the cockle may form the basis for a fish-

ery, being more efficient as a converter of plant to animal protein than the bullock or the cow.

Apart from the occasional large algae attached to isolated pebbles and rocks, which may incidentally provide attachment points for animals like *Mytilus*, the mussel, more typical of a rocky shore, some specialized higher plants may be found growing in the mud. These include *Spartina* (Cord Grass), *Ruppia* (Tas-

Above: **gulls taking off in the evening light from an estuary in Britain. Marshes and mud flats are a haven for shore birds, and thousands of them winter in estuaries and harbours.**

sel Pondweed), *Salicornia* (Glasswort) and *Halimione* (Sea Purslane). These plants all fulfil important roles in stabilizing the mud substrate and preventing it from erosion, and are also able to withstand the influence of salt.

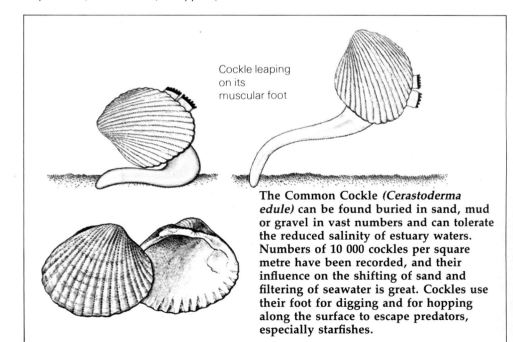

Cockle leaping on its muscular foot

The Common Cockle (*Cerastoderma edule*) can be found buried in sand, mud or gravel in vast numbers and can tolerate the reduced salinity of estuary waters. Numbers of 10 000 cockles per square metre have been recorded, and their influence on the shifting of sand and filtering of seawater is great. Cockles use their foot for digging and for hopping along the surface to escape predators, especially starfishes.

Lagoons

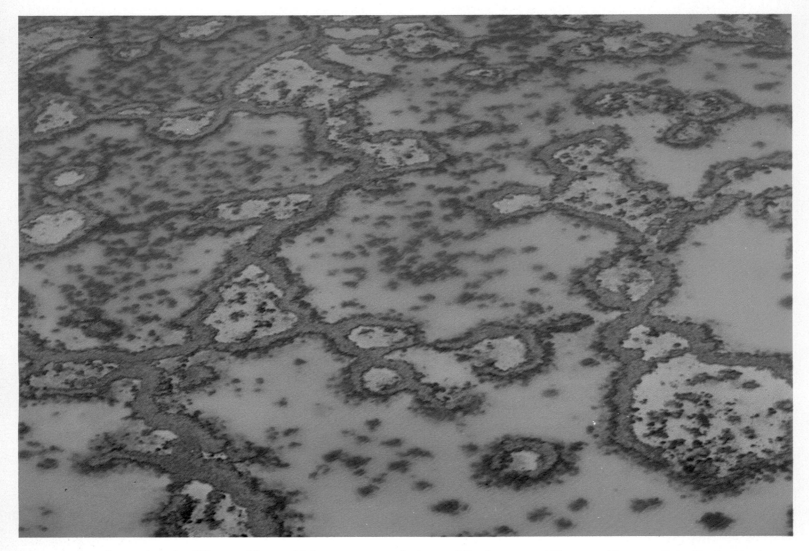

Lagoons occur in most parts of the world, some natural and some man-made. They are areas of shallow water lying within the protection of a reef, shingle beach, sand spit or artificial barrier. Some are entirely closed off from the sea but still filled with saline water. Because the water is shallow most of the lagoon bed will be illuminated, and because they are near the land there is often a good supply of mineral salts to the lagoon water, which ensures a supply of nutrients for marine plants. Therefore, lagoons sometimes support a great number of plants and animals. They are very vulnerable to pollution and man's influence, and the salinity of the water may be lowered by rain or raised by evaporation.

The fauna of lagoons is generally of marine origin, but those that are cut off from the sea may have peculiar animals dwelling in them, or at least animals that are not found in the open sea. For example, the Venice Lagoon contains some animals not found in the Adriatic Sea bordering it. One such is *Mysis relicta*

which was once a feature of freshwater lakes. After the last Ice Age, populations were cut off as the ice receded and the climate changed. Thus *Mysis relicta* may be found at Venice, in some central European lakes and in the northern Baltic Sea. Another inhabitant of the Venice Lagoon is the goby *Zosterisessor ophiocephalus*, which inhabits many shallow stretches of water with variable salinity along with the Three-spined Stickleback and the Lagoon Cockle *Cerastoderma glaucum*.

Tropical lagoons, sheltered by fringing reefs or the reefs of an atoll, present the greatest diversity of fauna. The waters in these lagoons rarely become diluted by rain, but their salinity may rise due to an increase in temperature and evaporation. Much of the fauna here is reef-related, but the large sand stretches may provide homes for remarkably patterned rays. Many juvenile reef fish inhabit the lagoons, where the conditions are suitable for their development. Small coral outcrops can occur, which diversify the fauna and habitats further.

Wistan reef lagoon, Great Barrier Reef, Australia. A maze of coral heads reach to the surface at low tide. The coral on the top is dead due to exposure to air, but growth continues on the sides.

Opposite page: **a lagoon fringed by coral reefs adjoining an island of French Polynesia, in the eastern Pacific.**

Mangrove communities

Mangrove trees not only stabilize the substratum in which they grow; they also provide a solid surface for certain animals to attach themselves to. In addition, terrestrial organisms living in adjoining woodland may colonize the branches of the mangrove trees. Thus a remarkable mixture of terrestrial and marine animals may be encountered in a mangrove swamp. The visitor to such an area will find that it contrasts rather sharply with the delights of a tropical sandy beach. Insects, often in vast numbers, may be the first animals to warrant attention. Other terrestrial animals include a great variety of birds; while some bats may live in the branches, as may tree-snakes.

Marine invertebrates too have found many niches in these swamps. The stabilized substrate is ideal for burrowing in, and because the mangroves prefer areas of siltation, there is an abundance of deposited organic material which serves as food. The floor of the swamp may be populated with various crabs such as the Fiddler Crab *Uca* and the Mangrove Crab *Sesarma*. There are generally great numbers of littorinid snails. Some, such as *Melaraphe scabra*, actually climb in the trees themselves and may be found in branches high above the water line. Pools on the floor of the swamp contain specialized fish living in burrows in the mud.

At high water many truly marine fish invade the mangrove swamp in search of food, and the importance of mangrove communities as nurseries for fish which as adults are of commercial or ecological consequence in the open sea is only just being appreciated.

In the Great Barrier Reef region of Australia and in New Guinea mangrove swamps provide a habitat for large marine crocodiles.

Animals typical of rocky shores sometimes occur on the roots and lower trunks of mangrove trees. Barnacles, oysters and sea-anemones have all been recorded, living in their typical style but on an unusual substratum.

The fact that such a diversity of life abounds in mangrove swamps raises important questions for the biologist. Have these habitats provided an evolutionary pathway for marine animals to colonize the land? The answer is in general likely to be that they have not. On the other hand, the fact that so many animals can live in such a habitat indicates that it must be very productive and that a great deal of food is available there.

Until recently mangroves have attracted little scientific attention. Since they are now regarded as a natural resource, scientists are paying more attention to them, particularly in countries where resources are scarce.

Two mud skippers 'rub noses' on the edge of a mangrove pool. These fish have eyes on top of the head, an ideal arrangement for seeing just above the water's surface. The pectoral fins are modified to serve as primitive legs to help movement out of the water, where these fish can survive a while.

Opposite, above right: a number of sedentary invertebrates, including oysters, sea-anemones and barnacles make use of the firm surfaces of mangrove roots for a place to dwell.

Opposite, below right: the fiddler crabs scuttle about on the mud of mangrove swamps. The greatly enlarged nipper is used for signalling and in combat between rivals.

Corals

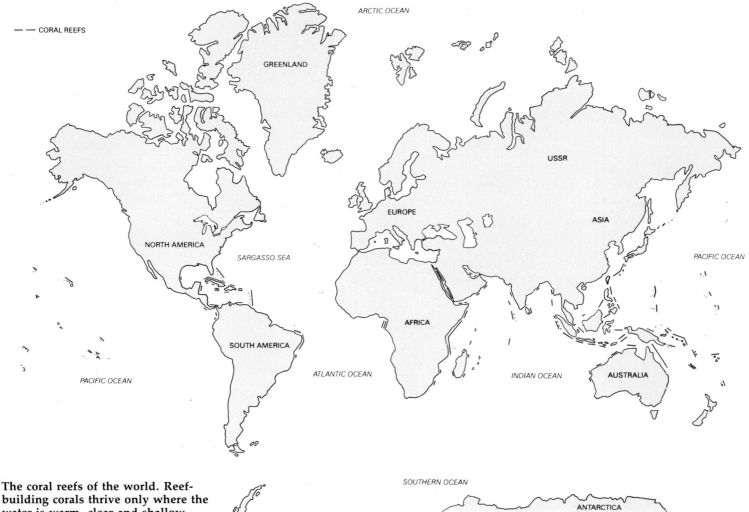

ARCTIC OCEAN

GREENLAND

USSR

EUROPE

ASIA

NORTH AMERICA

SARGASSO SEA

PACIFIC OCEAN

AFRICA

PACIFIC OCEAN

SOUTH AMERICA

ATLANTIC OCEAN

INDIAN OCEAN

AUSTRALIA

SOUTHERN OCEAN

ANTARCTICA

The coral reefs of the world. Reef-building corals thrive only where the water is warm, clear and shallow.

Coral reefs are formed from the accumulation of chalky skeletons of reef-building corals and associated organisms, which have become bound into ridge-like or bank-like offshore formations. Corals are not the only animals which build reefs: some of the polychaete worms do so with the accumulation of their protective tubes, but corals are by far the most conspicuous reef-builders. Coral reefs occur in waters where the temperature seldom falls below 22°C and never below 18°C. A glimpse at the map of the world will show that they are best developed on the eastern seaboards of continents where the water is overlying a continental shelf. They are virtually absent from the western coasts: a current chart shows that cold water from the Antarctic tends to flow up the western coasts of South Africa and South America, rendering the physical conditions too severe. On the other hand the eastern seaboards of these continents are bathed in warmer water which has passed through the equatorial regions before reaching land.

The coral polyps themselves belong to the class Anthozoa of the phylum Cnidaria (see page 32). Coral polyps are like sea-anemones but they secrete a cup-like outer skeleton to surround and protect the bottom part of the polyp. These polyps sit in their skeletal cup rather as an egg does in an egg cup. The skeleton

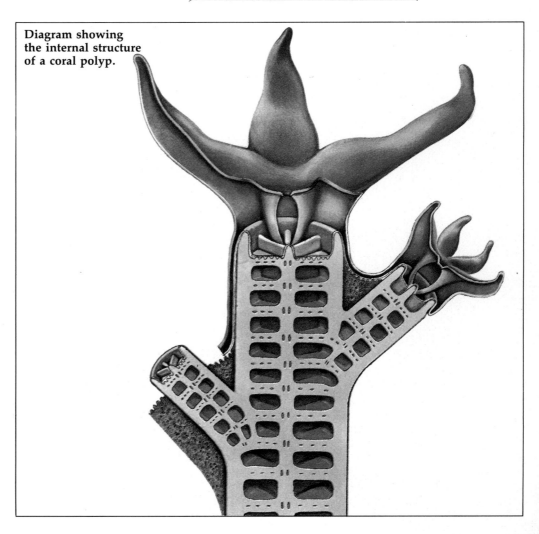

Diagram showing the internal structure of a coral polyp.

Alcyonium palmatum

Parerythropodium coralloides

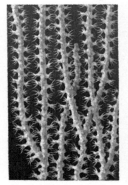

Left: a soft coral, *Xenia*; although not itself a reef-building coral this species may be quite prolific on coral reefs.

Eunicella verrucosa   Eunicella singularis

Boscia anglicum   Balanophyllia regia

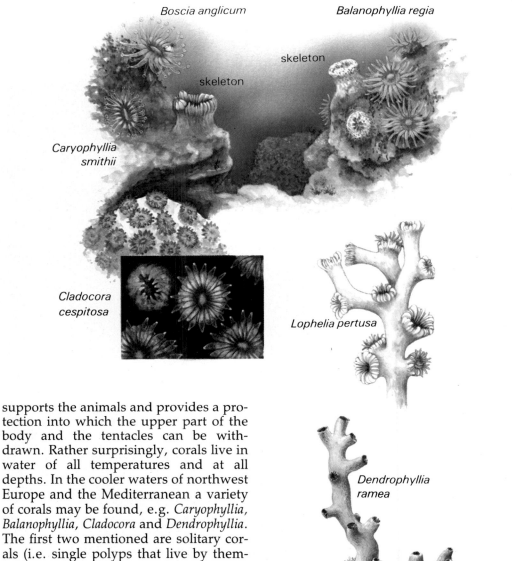

skeleton

skeleton

Caryophyllia smithii

Cladocora cespitosa

Lophelia pertusa

Dendrophyllia ramea

Corallium rubrum

Examples of soft corals (*Alcyonium* and *Parerythropodium*), true corals (*Balanophyllia, Caryophyllia, Cladocora, Lophelia* and *Dendrophyllia*) and Gorgonians (*Eunicella* and *Corallium*); All of these may be found even in the relatively cool waters of the Mediterranean.

supports the animals and provides a protection into which the upper part of the body and the tentacles can be withdrawn. Rather surprisingly, corals live in water of all temperatures and at all depths. In the cooler waters of northwest Europe and the Mediterranean a variety of corals may be found, e.g. *Caryophyllia, Balanophyllia, Cladocora* and *Dendrophyllia*. The first two mentioned are solitary corals (i.e. single polyps that live by themselves), whereas the second two mentioned form colonies of many individuals sharing a common skeletal mass. None of these is a reef-builder, and they all have relatively slow mechanisms for producing the calcium carbonate necessary for the skeleton. Reef-building corals have minute single-celled algae living inside their tissues, and these plants

appear to assist in the process of skeleton formation as well as possibly in the supply of nutrients to the coral polyp, although there is some discussion over this point.

The word coral has been rather loosely applied in the past. It was used by the Romans to refer to the semi-precious branching colonies of *Corallium rubrum* to be found in the Mediterranean and adjacent waters. This animal is actually a close relative of the sea-fans such as *Eunicella* and the Dead Man's Fingers like *Alcyonium*, and with the aid of a lens its tentacles will be seen to have minute side branches. It is not important as a reef-dwelling animal, although its relatives the 'soft' corals such as *Xenia* do contribute to the fauna of reefs and are quite dominant in some areas.

Theories of reef formation

During his historic voyage around the world in HMS Beagle, Charles Darwin made a study of coral reefs and their geological origins. He put forward a theory which was later supported by T. F. Dana. This mechanism, now known as the Darwin/Dana Subsidence Theory, states that because reef-building corals grow towards the light they will develop on seabeds where the illumination is sufficient, and should the seabed subside due to geological upheavals, the reef will continue to grow upwards towards the surface. In this way Darwin explains the occurrence of reefs near to land as well as those on far-off submerged sea mounts. This theory has many supporters, but there is one other which rivals it – Daly's Glacial Control Theory. Daly's argument is that the levels of water in the oceans have changed, and not the levels of the seabed. Daly believes that when the last Ice Age occurred, vast masses of fresh water were abstracted from the oceans to form the polar ice sheets, thus lowering the levels of the oceans. The forces of erosion cut out new shore platforms which were then im-

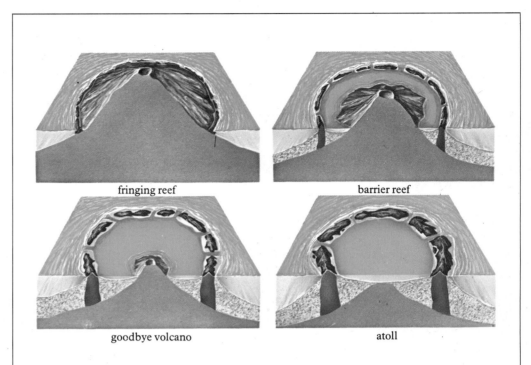

fringing reef

barrier reef

goodbye volcano

atoll

Darwin's theory of atoll formation. It is known that volcanoes along the mid-oceanic ridge will sink into the sea, so that what starts out as a fringing reef may well become a barrier reef and, eventually, an atoll.

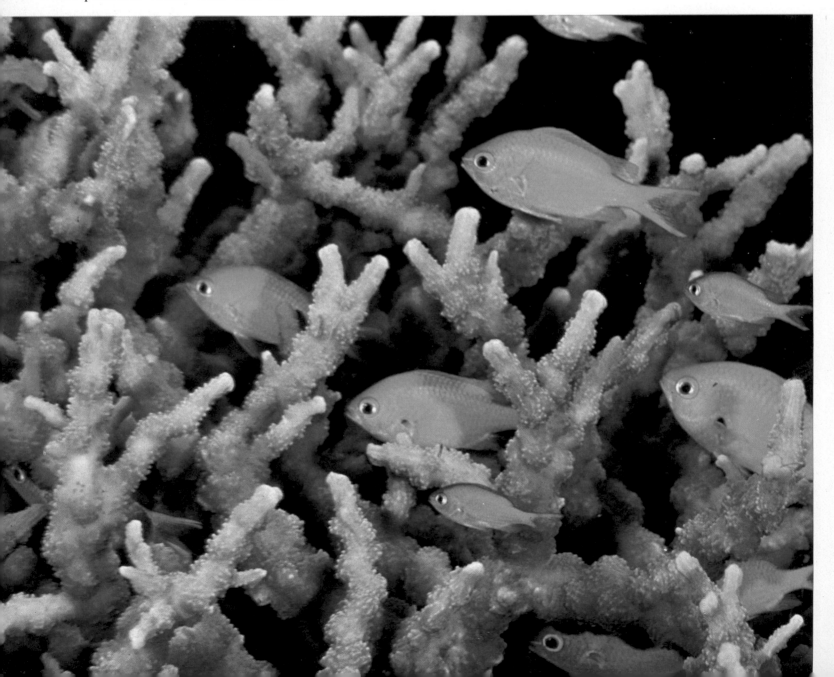

mersed when the ice caps began to melt. These platforms provided a suitable substrate for corals to grow on, especially as the seas were getting warmer with the retreat of the ice caps; then as the water levels rose the corals grew up keeping pace, thus remaining in the light.

There is no doubt that reef-building corals are dependent on the light. If they are smothered with sediments, or kept in the dark, the pace of calcification is slowed or stopped completely.

Scientists today recognize patch reefs, fringing reefs, barrier reefs and atolls, the last three of which were recognized by Darwin. Patch reefs are often small, and occur where the sea is relatively shallow. They are rather like small flat-topped hills and if they have developed in sheltered conditions their features are reasonably constant all round. Fringing reefs develop on the seabed as it slopes gently away from the shore. They may be very close to the land – a matter of metres – or they may lie a kilometer or more from it. They have a relatively steep seaward profile, where the force of the wave action is taken; and they are capped by a zone of severe physical conditions known as the algal ridge, where wave action and exposure to air and sun at low tide impose severe restrictions on the development of all but the toughest organisms. Behind lies a zone referred to as the 'rubble zone', consisting of broken colonies of coral washed over the reef from the vigorously growing colonies at the reef front. A variety of fishes and invertebrates live in the rubble zone. Behind this is usually a lagoon.

A barrier reef is similar to a fringing reef, but it usually grows at the outer edge of the continental shelf and may thus be a long way from land. Darwin believed that fringing reefs could develop into barrier reefs by the subsidence of the seabed, which would place the reef in deeper and deeper water as well as further away from land. Atolls are special reef systems growing up on the periphery of submerged volcanos or other sea mounts. The illustrations on the opposite page show how they could arise.

Opposite page, bottom: **the reef-forming coral provides protection for many thousands of different animals, including Damsel Fishes which seek protection in branching corals.**

Below: **massive corals in a tidal lagoon.**

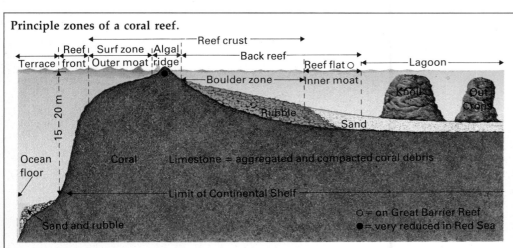

Principle zones of a coral reef.

Types of reef

The greatest difference in reefs and their faunas lies between the tropical systems of the Atlantic Ocean (largely restricted to the Caribbean and Gulf of Mexico, together with the reefs to the north of Brazil and those of the offshore islands like Bermuda) on the one hand, and the extensive reef systems of the Indo-west Pacific (stretching from the Red Sea via East Africa and the islands of the Indian Ocean to Indonesia, North Australia and the Pacific Island) on the other. In the Indo-west Pacific we find a coral system much older than that of the Atlantic. Here many species have evolved and not been subjected to dramatic changes of temperature or other catastrophes. The fauna is rich and varied, and of great age. In the Atlantic the reef fauna is younger and more restricted.

The process of reef-formation involves the recruitment of corals into the area. Reef-building corals have planktonic larvae which can travel over considerable distances in the surface water of the oceans. In suitable conditions they can settle, thrive and grow, feeding on minute animals and any input from their symbiotic plants. Equally, there will be many animals that feed directly or indirectly upon the coral polyps, or that will damage growing colonies in pursuit of other food. Scientists have recently been able to study the development of reefs using artificial reefs made of old car bodies, tyres or piles of stone.

These experimental studies have indicated that the first animals to arrive are often the soft corals. Then the faster-growing branching coral colonies are more likely to establish themselves and form the reef community proper. The slower-growing massive rounded forms arrive later. Situation and level of exposure also determine what types of coral can survive in a particular position or zone on a reef. Surprisingly, perhaps, the rounded massive types of coral such as the brain corals (genus *Meandrina*), are less able to survive in exposed positions than are the branching types such as members of the genus *Acropora*. The large single polyps of *Fungia*, the mushroom coral, are attached only as juveniles and unlike the reef-builders proper break free as they grow, and lie on the limestones of the coral reef.

Violent storms such as cyclones and hurricanes can whip up mountainous seas in the tropics and the devastation that these may cause on reefs is enormous. The manner in which various reef-dwellers assist in reef-breakdown is discussed on the following pages.

The relative variety of certain animal groups inhabiting coral reefs of the Atlantic and the Indo-west Pacific. It will be seen that the fauna of the latter regions is both more abundant and more diverse. The shaded areas indicate the abundance of coral genera making up the reef: nowhere in the Atlantic does the number exceed 50 genera.

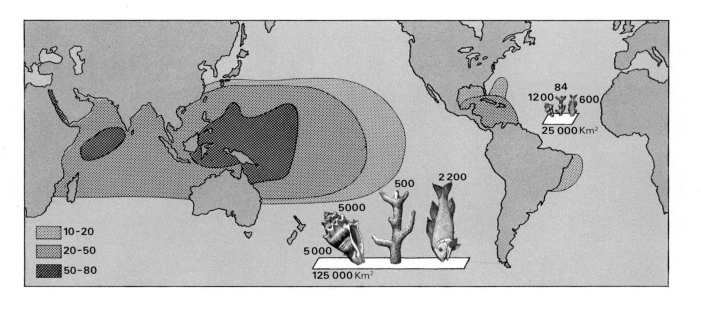

84
1200 600
25 000 Km²

500   2 200
5000

10-20
20-50
50-80

5000
125 000 Km²

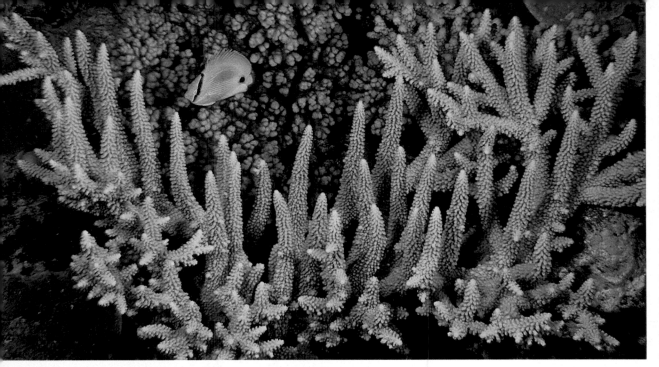

Left: Aeropora species are often the dominant branching corals of reefs. They provide living spaces between their branches for many small fish such as Damsel Fish. Others like the Butterfly Fish shown here hunt minute prey between the branches.

Below: This picture shows the different zones of a fringing reef surrounding a sand cay. The breaking waves wash the surf zone and in from this is the reef crest. Behind the crest lies the lagoon.

Left: Different forms of true coral. The massive brain coral has a rounded form with many irregularly outlined polyps which interlink to cover the surface of the colony, giving it a superficial similarity to part of the human brain.

Reef-dwelling animals

Most of the animals living on a reef are directly or indirectly dependent on the corals for food and shelter. Each reef species has a particular role in the life of the community. The molluscs are a conspicuous group, represented particularly by the snails and sea-slugs. The best known of these are the cowries and the cone-shells. Many of these are nocturnal feeders that may be found lurking under rocks by day. The cones in particular are efficient predators, and have highly toxic venom which they use to subdue their prey; this ranges from other snails, including cones, even to fish. The sea-slugs are often ornately coloured. Their bodies might at first appear attractive to predators such as fish, but their protection lies in their foul taste, so that if picked up they are usually spat out. The echinoderms are well represented. Starfish of many shapes and colours can be found. The bright blue *Linckia* of the Great Barrier Reef is very conspicuous and can be seen by day in shallow surface waters. The Crown-of-thorns Starfish *Acanthaster planci* became notorious in the 1960s as a coral predator. This starfish, which feeds directly on coral polyps, can occur from time to time in very dense populations, which by their combined feeding may kill off large numbers of reef-building coral colonies. Research has shown that reefs are, able to recover from such attacks more quickly than had at first been im-

Illustrated here and on the opposite page are some of the beautifully patterned fishes typical of reef waters. The patterns serve not only for camouflage but also for recognition within and between species, as well as showing courtship and breeding intentions.

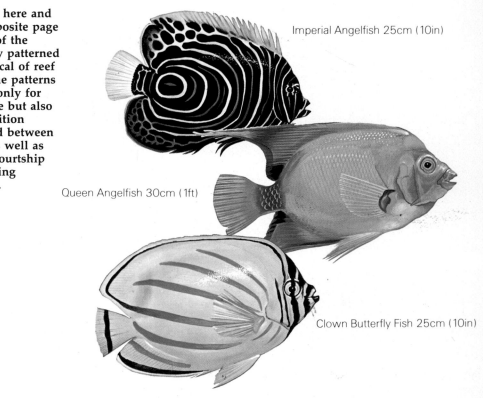

Imperial Angelfish 25cm (10in)

Queen Angelfish 30cm (1ft)

Clown Butterfly Fish 25cm (10in)

Below: the Cleaner Shrimp *(Stenopus hispidus)* is strikingly marked, and this aids recognition by fishes which may need to be cleaned.

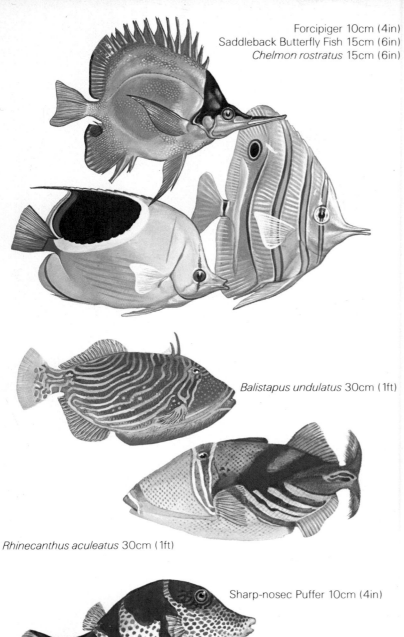

Forcipiger 10cm (4in)
Saddleback Butterfly Fish 15cm (6in)
Chelmon rostratus 15cm (6in)

Balistapus undulatus 30cm (1ft)

Rhinecanthus aculeatus 30cm (1ft)

Sharp-nosec Puffer 10cm (4in)

American Cowfish 23cm (9in)

Porcupine Fish 30cm (1ft)

Above: **the Crown-of-thorns Starfish (Acanthaster planci), which feeds on the tissues of living corals, sometimes destroying great numbers of them.**

Below: **the Giant Clam (Tridacna gigas) is the largest known living bivalve.**

agined. The Long-spined Sea-urchin *Diadema* can also destroy coral polyps by browsing on them with its teeth, but it also feeds on a variety of encrusting plants and animals. Small crowns of coloured, spirally arranged tentacles mark the site of polychaete worms living inside the coral colonies. The Cleaner Shrimp *Stenopus hispidus* is conspicuously marked by banding. This enables it to be readily identified by fish suffering from parasites, which swim up to it and then posture themselves in such a way that the shrimp may even enter their mouths to remove the offending object. The Cleaner Wrasse (*Labroides*) which is characterized by horizontal blue and black lines, swims over its 'patient' in order to remove parasites and growths. Interestingly it has a mimic, the Sabre-tooth Blenny (*Aspidonotus*) which looks very similar and which sick fish mistake for the cleaner. However the blenny is a predator which swims up to the 'patient', bites a piece out of its fins and swims away. The Clown Fish *Amphiprion* can live in the maw of a sea-anemone *Stoichactis*: it cloaks itself with mucus from the anemone and is not vulnerable to stings. Parrot fish are able to attack coral with their massive teeth, leaving characteristic tooth marks on it. There are many species of parrot fish and they make a colourful contribution to the reef. At night some species secrete a mucus 'sleeping bag', which envelops them as they sleep and possibly reduces odours from their bodies, which may otherwise attract predators such as cone shells.

The seashore in commerce

Seashores round the world are of great commercial importance. Their primary significance lies in their recreational use: in temperate regions the seashore in summer throngs with visitors. In parts of the world like the Mediterranean, East Africa, North Australia and the Caribbean, great tourist industries are based on the demand for a holiday by the sea. Recently, the increased popularity of SCUBA diving has placed the coral reefs of the Red Sea, Australia and Central America in this category too. Many of these natural areas are vulnerable to the presence of too many people, to say nothing of the pollution of the sea itself caused by the necessary support facilities. Visitors can cause considerable damage to branching reef corals by trampling, and it can take a number of years for them to recover. Other faunas can also suffer in this way.

Shores are under pressure from developers, not just for housing or holiday accommodation, but for facilities such as new harbour installations, location for airports as far away as possible from centres of habitation, and for industrial sites with ease of access for sea-going vessels. To this may be added the risks from mining and quarrying as well as offshore oil exploration. In many developing countries coral limestone is a convenient building material and can be extracted by direct blasting, causing immeasurable damage in the coral reef community which may have taken years to develop. The extraction of marine aggregates offshore may affect coastal currents and change the nature of the shore itself; and the effects of oil spills are well known.

Fisheries represent an obvious commercial use of the shore, but in fact relatively little fishing takes place on the shore itself. Shellfisheries exploit shore environments – winkles, cockles, clams, shrimps and sea-urchins are some examples; but some of these animals take a number of years to grow and are not easily replaced. Many tropical lagoons form the basis for important prawn fisheries. Reefs are used extensively by tropical fishermen seeking snappers, groupers and other commercial fish.

Less appreciated, but potentially very important, are the harvests of kelps and certain invertebrates like soft corals and sponges for the extraction of pharmaceuticals. Drug researchers have recently been testing a whole range of organisms to investigate their potential as sources of medically important substances. Some invertebrates such as sponges and semi-precious corals are important in their own right.

From this brief account it will be appreciated that the seashores of the world and their inhabitants, plant and animal, are under great pressure from man. In order that successive generations may enjoy them it is vital that this exploitation be controlled. Further, it is important that the pollutants which threaten the shores, both from land-based sources such as industrial plants as well as sea-borne sources such as shipping, be stringently monitored and controlled.

Above: **cockle fishing on the south coast of England.**

The seashore in the study of biology

The shore is one of the finest places to study animals, because representatives of almost all known groups are to be found there and are readily accessible to the observer. Marine animals are of great evolutionary interest, because some show life-styles and bodily architecture which has endured in the oceans of the world since the dawn of life. Others show how these styles have become modified and advanced under the pressures of natural selection (survival of the fittest) to produce the efficient and dominant life-forms which we see today. Members of phyla such as the molluscs, the brachiopods and the echinoderms include forms which have remained relatively unaltered for millions of years, as well as species which have undergone great evolutionary advancement. The molluscs are an old group: before the advent of the fishes, the squids ruled the oceans; and although they are declining somewhat, they still show superb adaptations to swimming life. They have solved problems such as vision and buoyancy in a manner quite different from the fishes, and this makes for most instructive comparisons.

Important information on the affinities of different groups of animals has been made available by comparing their life cycles and developmental stages. It is clear, for example, that although the adult sea-squirt and the adult fish are totally dissimilar, they are related because their developmental stages have some features in common. It is believed that the early fishes and the sea-squirts probably arose from common ancestors. Similarities in development and larval forms have indicated a number of affinities in the animal kingdom which would have been quite difficult to establish if only terrestrial forms were available for comparisons. It was for this type of research that the Marine Laboratory was established at Naples in 1874.

Priorities in research have changed considerably since that time, and today much energy is being directed to the study of animals and plant cells, physiology and ecology. Nevertheless much is to be learnt from marine animals, to say nothing of improved methods of fish-rearing and fish-catching. Today most nations have a marine laboratory of some description, and scientists working in them are responsible for producing much important literature.

It is thought that the sea holds the key to many evolutionary secrets. The deeper waters of the ocean abyss are virtually inaccessible, but the shallower waters of the seashore still have enormous research potential, and much effort is concentrated here. This photograph shows an acorn worm feeding on organic rubbish in shallow water. The acorn worms provide a fascinating insight into the early development of the chordates as the adults of this group have a primitive backbone whilst the larvae resemble echinoderm larvae.

Conclusion

It is not surprising that different attitudes to exploitation and conservation of seashore life prevail in different countries, and in some cases there is legislation affecting what may or may not be permitted in the way of collecting specimens or what type of fishing methods may be used.

It should always be remembered that certain species are in particular danger from man's activities. Organisms such as corals and large territorial fishes have been greatly over-fished. They are easily caught and exploited. Other species may be far less in danger.

If you are exploring the rocky shore remember that you may have to work hard to discover some animals living in crevices and under boulders. If you have to turn stones over please remember to turn them back afterwards, so that animals which have chosen to live underneath in the dark may continue to do so after your visit.

Snorkel and SCUBA divers are privileged to see animal and plant life 'at home', but should remember that they too can disturb the environment greatly. Some invertebrates like the large and attractive gastropods take years to reach maturity and reproduce. They are vulnerable to curio-hunters. It is also to be hoped that the use of spear guns will be kept to a minimum and certainly that they will not be used against territorial fish which hide in holes and which thus make easy targets.

If you are collecting specimens for a purpose, arrange to look after them carefully. Prevent them from becoming overheated by placing your jars in rock pools to keep the temperature down. Put the lids on only when actually carrying the jars and add just sufficient water to cover the specimens or let them swim freely. Only take the animals away from the beach if you are certain that you can keep them alive. After you have examined them return them to the spot they came from, or to a similar place.

Glossary

Antenna usually a long, slender, sensory appendage on the heads of some arthropods and some annelids.

Asexual describes organisms which reproduce without sexual processes.

Asymmetrical without symmetry, being irregular or unequal: used to describe the growth form of some animals, e.g. certain sponges.

Benthic dwelling in or on the seabed.

Brackish describes water usually containing less, but occasionally more, salt than is usually found in the sea.

Byssus hair-like filaments which attach some bivalves to rocks or plants.

Calcareous being made of calcium carbonate or chalk.

Cell smallest functional unit of a plant or animal, consisting of a nucleas surrounded by cytoplasm and bounded by a membrane, and sometimes a cell wall.

Cephalothorax region combining the head and thoracic segments of advanced crustaceans.

Chela leg of crustaceans which bears pincers or nippers.

Chordate animal with at least a simple form of backbone (the notochord) at some stage in the life cycle: includes the vertebrates.

Class major subdivision of a phylum.

Coelom fluid-filled cavity, formed within the middle cell layer of animals.

Detritus particles of decaying organisms accumulating, for example, on the seabed; forms the food of many invertebrate animals.

Disc (of an anemone) either the mouth disc which bears the tentacles, or the basal, suckerlike attachment disc; (of an ophiuroid) body excluding the arms.

Dorsal upper side of a bilaterally symmetrical animal (c.f. Ventral).

Epiphyte plant which grows on the outer surface of another organism.

Evert turn inside out, often applied to the process of extending the proboscis of worms.

Exhalent breathing out, applied to respiratory streams of water in organisms or the anatomical structures by which they are conveyed.

Free-living living unattached to any other structure.

Frond (of alga) all of the plant except the holdfast.

Gamete sperm or egg.

Gametophyte (of plants) generation which produces sperms and eggs.

Genus group of related species; many genera may form one order.

Holdfast attachment organ of seaweeds.

Inhalent breathing in; applied to respiratory streams of water in organisms or the anatomical structures by which they are conveyed.

Invertebrate without a backbone.

Lamella thin, plate-like structure or layer.

Larva developmental phase of an organism which usually does not resemble the adult or lead a way of life similar to it; a phase often associated with an entirely different manner of feeding from the adult and which provides a dispersive mechanism in many sedentary marine species; always terminates with the process of metamorphosis.

Mangrove refers either to trees or shrubs of the genus *Rhizophora* (or a related one) growing on the seashore or shallow water, or alternatively to the complex community formed by the mangrove plant.

Mantle special region of the body wall, particularly of molluscs, which secretes the shell and encloses the mantle cavity.

Medusa the jellyfish phase in the life cycle of hydrozoan and scyphozoan cnidarians.

Metamorphosis the act of transformation of a larva into an adult.

Neap tide tide with the smallest range between high and low water.

Nematocyst special cell of cnidarians which discharges threads to sting or ensnare the prey.

Notochord skeletal tube running from front to back in some simple chordates; forerunner of the backbone of vertebrates.

Oral relating to the mouth; in echinoderms that side of the body on which the mouth is situated (c.f. Aboral).

Order major subdivision of a class.

Paragaster main cavity inside a sponge.

Parasitism condition whereby one organism, the parasite, lives on or in another, its host, at the expense of the latter.

Pelagic inhabiting the surface waters of the sea.

Perisarc thin, tubular, skeletal structure investing the outer surface of many hydroid polyps.

Phylum major division of the animal kingdom which includes those animals thought to have a common evolutionary origin.

Phytoplankton planktonic plants (generally microscopic).

Plankton drifting organisms or swimming organisms which are not able to determine their position in the sea.

Planula simple larva (for instance) of cnidarians resembling a ball of cells, usually ciliated and hence able to move.

Pneumatophore organ of flotation containing gas, or a modified individual in a siphonophoran colony which serves this function.

Polyp sedentary individual cnidarian such as *Hydra*, basically with a sac-like body opening only by the mouth which is generally surrounded by tentacles.

Proboscis special structure at the anterior end of some animals; in nemertines it is generally everted through the mouth but is itself not part of the alimentary canal; in polychaetes it is everted through the mouth and is part of the alimentary canal.

Radula small, horny, tongue-like strip bearing teeth; used by many molluscs for rasping food.

Rhizoid root-like structure.

Salinity measure of the salt concentration of water.

Sessile commonly meaning living attached to a structure such as a rock or a shell of another organism.

Siphon tube leading into or out of the bodies of invertebrates and used for conducting water currents, found especially in molluscs and sea-squirts.

Species reproductively isolated group of interbreeding organisms; usually defined by morphological characteristics.

Spicule minute fragment or crystal of skeletal material.

Splash zone zone on the shore above the highest point to which the tides flow but which is under the influence of spray and salt-water.

Spore minute reproductive germ or particle produced by the asexually reproductive spores; alternates with the gametophyte.

Spring tide tide with the greatest range between high and low water.

Stolon root-like structure found in some animals and linking up individuals in a colony; in plants a horizontal branch which produces its own roots and subsequently a new individual.

Sublittoral biologically defined zone on the seashore which lies below the highest point to which laminarians grow, and only uncovered at the lowest tides and extending down from the shore to the shallow seabed; equivalent to the term lower shore as used in this book.

Symbiotic describes an organism of one species which lives in close association with one of another species and to the advantage of both.

Test shell of a sea-urchin or starfish which, strictly speaking is an internal skeleton.

Thallus entire body of a lower plant, such as an alga or lichen.

Tube-foot hydraulic appendage of echinoderms and part of the water vascular system.

Ventral underside of a bilaterally symmetrical animal (c.f. dorsal).

Vertebrate animal with a backbone made up of vertebrae.

Water vascular system hydraulic system unique to the echinoderms comprising a system of vessels and organs like the tube-feet, and fulfilling various functions, especially locomotion.

Zonation separation of plants and animals into discrete zones or communities on the shore related to the tidal levels.

Zooid individual animal in a colony; usually applied to the Cnidaria and Ectoprocta.

Zooplankton animals of the plankton.

Index